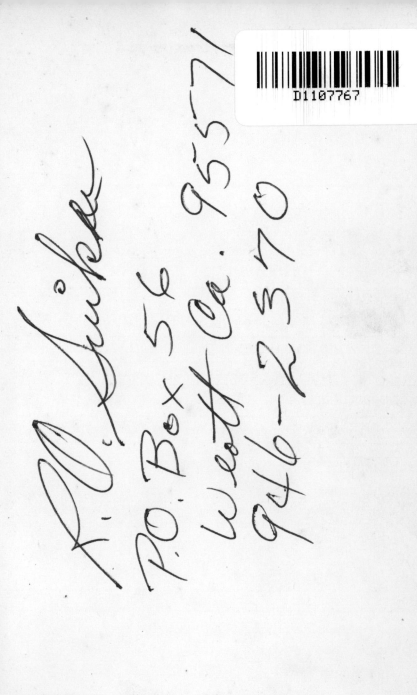

R. D. Luiken
P.O. Box 56
West, Ca. 95571
946-2370

This Book is the property of

**With the Compliments of John Deere,
Manufacturer of Quality Farm
Equipment for Over a Century**

The Trade-Mark of Quality

Made Famous by Good Implements

The

Operation, Care, and Repair

...*of*...

Farm Machinery

TWENTY-SECOND EDITION

Published by

JOHN DEERE

Moline, Illinois

Contents

Preface

IN the study of modern farming and modern farming methods, an understanding of the operation, care, and repair of farm implements becomes increasingly important as farming becomes more highly mechanized. The farmer of today and the future, with machines of greater working capacities, must have a more thorough knowledge of mechanics than did his ancestors whose farming equipment was limited to a comparatively few simple implements requiring few adjustments.

The high schools and agricultural colleges of the United States are doing a very commendable work in teaching farm mechanics to the young men who will be the farmers and agricultural leaders of tomorrow. The activity of these institutions in encouraging the use of more efficient machines and in teaching the proper methods of adjustment and operation of all farm implements is certain to result in the lowering of production costs throughout the agricultural industry.

It is the purpose of this book to assist instructors in farm mechanics in giving a thorough and practical course in the operation, care, and repair of the more important farm machines. It is designed especially for those who make a study of farm mechanics in high schools, colleges, and short courses with the expectation of applying the knowledge gained to actual farming or to the instruction of others.

The unqualified endorsement given the earlier editions of this book by educators the country over led to the production of this, the twenty-second edition. It is the hope of the publisher that this more thorough and complete textbook will be of even greater value than its predecessors in filling the need for a complete text dealing only with the operation, care, and repair of farm machines.

The publisher wishes to express appreciation to high school instructors in agriculture, agricultural college professors, and state supervisors of agricultural education for the assistance and suggestions so generously given in the preparation of this and previous editions.

JOHN DEERE

Part One
POWER ON THE FARM

Mechanical power made its first appearance on the American farm late in the nineteenth century. To be sure, power in the form of steam traction engines, used primarily for operating the threshing rig, was in use some years before, yet the first real trend to farm-owned power began about Spanish-American war times. It gained great impetus from that time, principally on the larger farms where the standard type tractor was used for field work such as plowing, disking, seeding, and harvesting.

With the advent of the general-purpose tractor, the trend to power farming was a definite march, for with his general-purpose tractor the farmer had power adaptable to all of his farm jobs including planting and cultivating as well as drawbar and belt jobs. The constant improvement of the general-purpose tractor and its ever-broadening adaptability have

Figure 1—A general-purpose tractor with two-bottom plow controlled by tractor power lift through remote cylinder.

made tractors of this type the most widely-used power on farms today.

It is due, largely, to the improvement of the general-purpose tractor that the tractor is the principal source of power on many farms throughout the Nation. It has aided materially in cutting production costs, increasing the working capacity of the farm worker, and speeding up farm operations. The remarkable increase in the number of tractors on farms in the past is an indication of what may be expected in the future as tractors and tractor-operated machines are developed to an even higher state of efficiency and practicability for farms of all sizes.

The general-purpose tractor of today, built in a wide variety of styles, sizes, and power capacities, provides the farmer with power for all farm jobs—plowing, disking, planting, cultivating, mowing, and all other major operations including belt work. The need for horses is practically eliminated where tractors of this type are used.

Recent years also have brought a better and more general knowledge among farmers of the factors that govern the

Figure 2—General-purpose tractor planting four rows of corn.

operation and care of internal-combustion engines. This factor, combined with the great improvement in tractor design, has resulted in more satisfactory performance of farm power units and less expense for repairs and service.

Before attempting to operate a tractor or engine, the operator should make a careful and thorough study of the instruction books furnished by the manufacturer. Although the general principles that govern their operation are the same, each make of tractor or engine has somewhat different operating problems. The basic principles, common to practically all internal-combustion engines used on the farm, will be discussed in the following pages.

Internal-Combustion Engines. An internal-combustion engine is an engine in which the heat or pressure energy necessary to produce motion is developed in the engine cylinder, as by the explosion of a gas, and not in a separate chamber as in a steam engine boiler. The fuel, mixed with air, ignites, burns rapidly, expands inside the cylinder, pushes the piston back, turns the crankshaft, and so develops power. The power generated can be applied to the operation of

Figure 3—Cultivating cotton with a two-row tractor cultivator.

machines through the belt pulley in the case of the engine, and through the belt pulley, drawbar, or power take-off in the standard-type tractor.

The modern general-purpose tractor is equipped with a hydraulic power lift which furnishes a fourth outlet for power which is used in raising and lowering integral equipment and, with remote cylinder, for raising, lowering, and adjusting drawn equipment.

There are two general types of internal-combustion engines —two-stroke cycle and four-stroke cycle. The two-stroke cycle engine has a power impulse or working stroke every revolution. The four-stroke cycle engine burns its fuel charge every second revolution. There are four strokes of the piston from one power impulse to the next. All farm engines and tractors are of the four-cycle type. These strokes are:

First: Suction or Intake. Here the piston draws a charge of fuel and air into the cylinder through the inlet valve.

Figure 4—Illustrating the four strokes of the four-stroke cycle.

Second: Compression. The piston, on its return, compresses the fuel and air mixture into the end of the cylinder called the combustion chamber. Full power is secured only with good compression.

Third: Expansion or Power Stroke. At a point slightly in advance of full compression, an electric spark, produced by a magneto or battery, ignites the fuel. This causes a sudden high expansion pressure to act on the piston, pushing it back so that work is performed.

Fourth: Exhaust. On its return from the power stroke, the piston pushes the burned gases out of the cylinder, through the open exhaust valve, and then through the exhaust manifold.

These events—suction or intake, compression, expansion or power, and exhaust—make the complete cycle.

Chapter I.
TRACTORS

Basically, the tractor is made up of: (1) the engine which is the source of power; (2) the transmission which makes this power available at the drawbar, power take-off, power lift, belt pulley, and which provides means for varying the forward speed to meet the job at hand and the condition encountered; (3) final drive (including the differential) which delivers the power from engine through transmission to the rear wheels; (4) clutch which acts as a coupling to connect the engine to the transmission and belt pulley. The efficiency of a tractor depends upon the proper functioning of all units —a condition which exists only when all units are properly maintained and properly adjusted.

For the discussion of this chapter, the tractor shown in Figs. 5 and 6 is used as a basis. It is a typical general-purpose farm tractor having a two-cylinder, horizontal engine available in two types: to burn the heavier fuels such as distillate, tractor fuel, and gasoline and, with increased compression ratio, to burn gasoline only.

When a new tractor is delivered, it is ready to give efficient service for a long time, under normal conditions, without a great amount of adjustment. The operator's chief responsibility is in correct lubrication and proper care. However, when trouble arises, the operator should be capable of analyzing his machine and making the day-to-day adjustments that fall within the range of his skill and the equipment of his farm shop.

The Engine. As the source of tractor power, the engine of the tractor is in operation during every minute the tractor is at work whether on drawbar, belt, or power take-off. For this reason, it is well to gain a thorough understanding of the essential requirements for most efficient engine operation.

Three elements are required for engine operation: (1) Fuel, (2) Air, and (3) Electrical energy or spark.

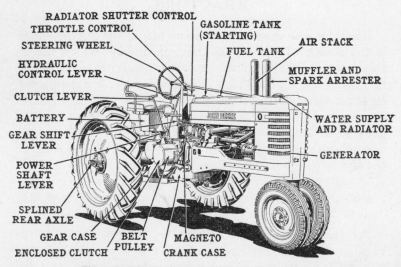

Figure 5—Adjustable tread general-purpose tractor.

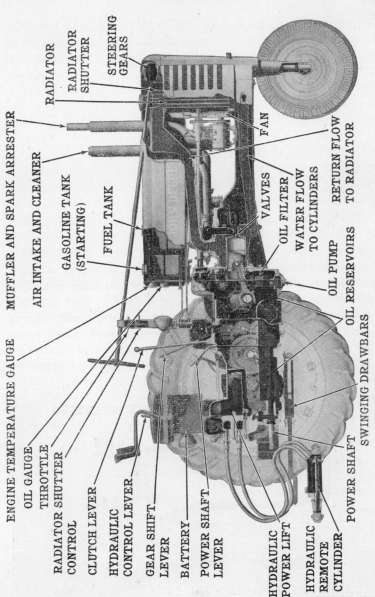

RADIATOR

RADIATOR SHUTTER

STEERING GEARS

MUFFLER AND SPARK ARRESTER

AIR INTAKE AND CLEANER

GASOLINE TANK (STARTING)

FUEL TANK

FAN

VALVES

OIL FILTER

WATER FLOW TO CYLINDERS

RETURN FLOW TO RADIATOR

OIL PUMP

OIL RESERVOIRS

ENGINE TEMPERATURE GAUGE

OIL GAUGE

THROTTLE

RADIATOR SHUTTER CONTROL

CLUTCH LEVER

HYDRAULIC CONTROL LEVER

GEAR SHIFT LEVER

BATTERY

POWER SHAFT LEVER

HYDRAULIC POWER LIFT

HYDRAULIC REMOTE CYLINDER

POWER SHAFT

SWINGING DRAWBARS

Figure 6—Cross-sectional view of the general-purpose tractor. Parts shown in color are oiled automatically.

In considering these three elements, it is wise to consider fuel and air at the same time, for the successful operation of the engine depends upon a correctly-proportioned mixture of fuel with air. The proportions are controlled by adjustment of needle valves on the carburetor. When the mixture is correct the engine runs smoothly, delivering its maximum power; too much fuel in the mixture, called a "rich" mixture, is indicated by a black, smoky exhaust and irregular running of the engine; too little fuel, called a "lean" mixture, is indicated by a "popping back" through the carburetor, misfiring of the engine, or by a high-pitched "ping" referred to as a pre-ignition knock.

The fuel system of the "all-fuel" tractor is shown below. It consists of the fuel tank, small tank for gasoline used in starting, a three-way fuel valve which permits flow of fuel from either tank, and a carburetor which serves to atomize the fuel in air to produce a highly combustible gas. The fuel system of the gasoline tractor differs in that a single tank is used, and the three-way valve is unnecessary. Gas is drawn into the combustion chambers, placed under pressure by the piston on its compression cycle, and ignited or burned by a spark, timed to fire at the proper instant to deliver full power of the burning fuel to the piston.

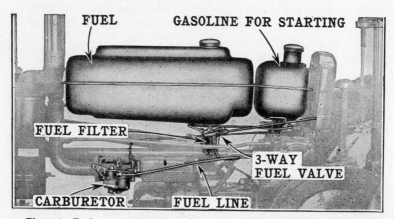

Figure 7—Fuel system showing principal parts that may require servicing.

When any one or more of the three essentials is deficient or lacking, the engine will operate poorly or fail entirely to operate. It is wise, therefore, to check the "important three" for lack of efficiency in the engine, difficult starting, or entire failure to start. In checking the tractor, start with first essentials first, and check through each possible source of trouble. This procedure eliminates guesswork and removes the need for "back tracking" in making the service check-up.

Checking Fuel System. The most important point in caring for and adjusting the fuel system is keeping out dust and dirt. Fuel should always be stored in clean containers, protected from dust, dirt, and water; it should always be strained when filling the tanks. When engine trouble occurs, it is well to look for the cause of the trouble in the fuel system first.

Check for fuel in both tanks. Then check three-way fuel valve for flow of fuel to the glass sediment bowl to be certain that both fuel for operating and gasoline for starting are available at the carburetor. Clean glass bowl when water or dirt is present. With fuel flow to carburetor verified, remove carburetor drain plug, open three-way valve, and drain water or operating fuel from carburetor. Make certain that starting fuel—gasoline—is flowing to carburetor.

Checking Air Cleaner. When we consider that every gallon of liquid fuel consumed by the engine must be mixed with nine thousand gallons of air, the importance of the air cleaner (Fig. 8) becomes apparent. The sole function of the air cleaner is to provide a continuous flow of clean air to the carburetor where it is mixed with the fuel and drawn into

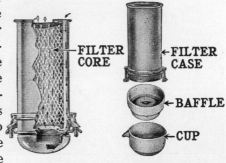

FILTER CORE ←FILTER CASE

←BAFFLE

←CUP

Figure 8—Air cleaner shown in cross-section and dissembled for servicing.

the combustion chamber. The air cleaner removes from incoming air, dust and grit particles that would injure the cylinders and working parts if drawn into the combustion chamber. The air is drawn into the cleaner through a high stack from such a level as to avoid the heavier, more harmful particles of dirt. The dust that passes through the stack is caught and retained in a mist of oil created by the draft of air drawn through the cleaner. Before each day's work, the oil sediment cup at base of filter should be detached, the dirt-filled oil removed, and the entire cup washed in gasoline or kerosene to remove all the sediment. The cup should then be refilled to bead mark with new engine oil and replaced. When engine difficulties occur, the air cleaner should be given a routine check since a clogged air cleaner, or a badly-dented or crimped air intake may so constrict the passage of air as to make engine operation impossible.

Ignition System. With fuel and air flow established, check the ignition system to make certain that a good "hot" spark reaches the compressed gas. To check for spark at the combustion chamber, remove spark plug wire and hold end 1/4-inch from the engine as shown in Fig. 9. Turn

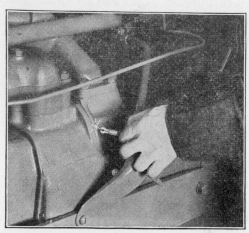

flywheel, or crank the engine. If sparks jump from end of wire to the engine, magneto and spark plug wires are in good condition; spark plugs are at fault and should be cleaned and respaced or replaced if worn beyond further service, or if cracks are apparent in the por-

Figure 9—Simple method for checking spark at spark plug.

celain insulator.

If no spark occurs upon checking at terminal, check magneto. Remove spark plug wires and in their place insert test wires formed of soft copper or steel wire. (See Fig. 10.) Place opposite end of test wire 1/4-inch from some metal part of magneto. Turn flywheel or crank; if sparks occur here, magneto is operating satisfactorily; it is evident then that spark plug wires are broken or badly frayed causing a short circuit which "grounds" the spark before it reaches the plug. Replace spark plug wires. If no sparks occur upon checking the magneto in this manner, remove magneto cap and check magneto points for proper clearance as given in your tractor instruction book or service manual. If points are pitted, burned, or dirty, they should be honed smooth and cleaned

Figure 10—Test wires, of soft copper or steel, in place on the magneto.

Figure 11—Magneto points should be honed smooth and adjusted to proper spacing.

thoroughly. (See Fig. 11.) Do not file magneto points.

With points replaced and properly gapped or spaced, check again by cranking the engine. If no sparks occur, remove magneto and take it to your tractor service dealer for repair. Magneto repairs call for a fine degree of skill and the use of special shop equipment; for this reason, it is unwise to attempt magneto repairs in the farm shop. When replacing the magneto, follow the manufacturer's instruction book for correct procedure to insure proper "timing" or firing order of the cylinders.

Compression. As mentioned previously, efficient engine operation depends upon proper mixture of fuel and air, proper

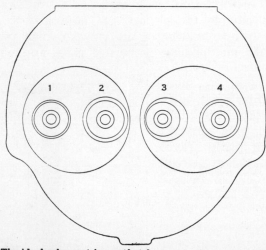

Figure 12—The ideal valve seat is one that forms a perfect seal of uniform width over the complete circumference of the valve-port. A seat too narrow (1) tends to cut or pound a groove in the valve, resulting in lost compression. With the seat too wide (2), it is almost impossible to get a perfect seal and, here again, loss of compression results.

Where the seat has been worn off center (3) due to worn valve guide or any other cause, it is impossible to obtain the proper seal between valve and seat which results in lost compression and uneven operation of the engine.

The properly seated valve (4) forms the perfect compression seal, and insures proper engine performance for the longest period. Width of seat varies with power and type of engine. See manufacturer's instruction book or consult your dealer for exact width for your engine.

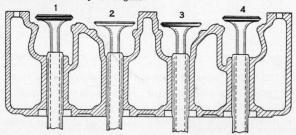

compression in the combustion chamber, and spark properly timed to ignite the mixture. We have discussed the method of checking the fuel system, the air flow to the carburetor, and the ignition system; compression should be the next point to be given consideration.

Proper compression requires a perfect seal of the combustion chamber which will insure full power from every charge of fuel entering the chamber. Two factors are involved in gaining the perfect seal necessary to efficient operation: proper seating of the valves (which permit intake of fuel and passage of burned gases and which are

Figure 13—Complete valve assembly is shown at the right with principal parts named. Note especially the many precision-fitted parts where wear may occur to cause mis-alignment of the entire assembly. In servicing valves, all parts must be given skilled attention if engine efficiency is to be restored.

In illustration below, note that wear at top and bottom of the valve guide has caused mis-alignment of the entire valve. Obviously, valve cannot be seated properly until valve guide has been replaced.

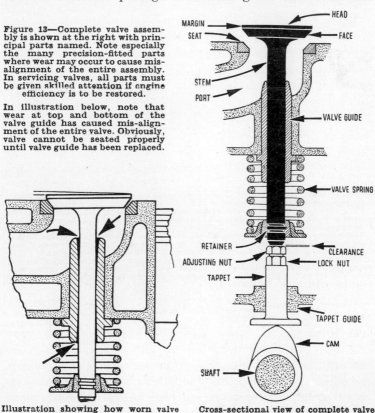

Illustration showing how worn valve guide affects proper seating.

Cross-sectional view of complete valve assembly with parts named.

"timed" to close at the time of the power stroke to seal the combustion chamber), and proper fit of pistons and piston rings which seal the chamber to prevent passage of gas and power between piston and cylinder wall.

As the piston moves forward in the cylinder, it compresses the air in the combustion chamber creating a "cushion" of air. When cranking the engine, this cushion will be noted as each piston approaches "dead center", or the end of its stroke. If no definite cushion or compression is noted at uniform intervals as the engine is cranked, weak compression is indicated.

Energy required to turn the engine should be alike for all cylinders indicating that compression is equal in all cylinders. If energy required to bring one piston over center, or "compression", is greater than that required for another,

or if a "hissing" sound indicating the escape of air is heard, compression is weak, with resultant loss of power under operating conditions.

The cause of poor compression may be found in poorly adjusted valves, improperly seated valves (see Fig. 12), worn valve guides (Fig. 13), worn piston rings or cylinder walls, or improperly sealed cylinder head gaskets which permit passage of air or water under

Figure 14—Thickness gauges should be used when adjusting valve tappet clearance.

pressure. Before attempting extensive repairs it is well to check the valves for proper tappet clearance and adjust tappets to tolerances recommended in the instruction book or service manual for your particular tractor. Thickness gauges should be used in determining proper clearance (see Fig. 14).

If restoring proper tappet clearance fails to restore compression, it is well to enlist the aid of a skilled tractor serviceman to restore the engine to full efficiency. While the actual principles of engine construction and function are simple, the servicing of such parts as valves, pistons, and piston rings of the modern precision-built tractor involves the use of highly specialized equipment which the average farmer would find unprofitable to install in his home shop. The use of special steels in valves dictates the use of special stones and facing tools in their servicing (see Fig. 15); likewise, the highly precise job of replacing pistons, piston pins, and piston rings which involves removing, and in many cases adjusting, pressure lubricated bearings, is one for which special tools have been developed.

The Cooling System. The purpose of the cooling system (Fig. 16) is to dissipate the heat of combustion and friction and to maintain proper

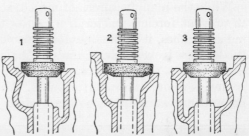

Figure 15—Special stones used in servicing valves. (1) Rough-cutting. (2) Rough stone used for narrowing the seat. (3) Fine stone for finishing.

engine temperature for most efficient engine performance. When we consider that temperature in the combustion chambers of a tractor under load may run as high as 1250 degrees Fahrenheit, the need for an adequate, efficient cooling system, properly maintained, is apparent.

The cooling system used on the tractor shown in Fig. 6, consists of a tubular radiator with a gear-driven fan. The circulation of the cooling water is thermo-siphon or temperature-controlled. When the cylinders warm up after starting the engine, the warmed water rises and is displaced by cooler water; the constantly rising warm water from the cylinders causes a circulation through the radiator, where the water is cooled by a blast of air drawn through the radiator by the fan.

Most present-day tractors are equipped with some device to increase or decrease the cooling area of the radiator. On the tractor shown, a shutter, adjustable from the seat of the tractor, is placed before the radiator to facilitate bringing the tractor quickly up to operating temperature and to maintain that temperature at all times.

The radiator consists mainly of a core of vertical tubes attached to which are fins that form extra cooling area. As the fan draws a steady current of air through the radiator, the water is cooled as it flows downward. Fig. 16 shows a cross-section of the cooling system.

While the manufacturers of most tractors provide screens to prevent foreign matter from entering and clogging the radiator tubes, it is the operator's responsibility to see that this screen is kept clean and to make certain that only clean water is placed in the radiator and that the water level is always above the radiator tubes. Water should never be poured into an empty cooling system when the engine is

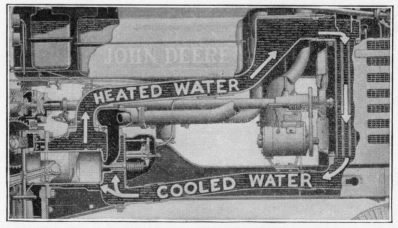

Figure 16—Cross-sectional view of the thermo-siphon cooling system.

hot, nor should cold water be poured into a hot engine, or hot water poured into a cold engine. Extremes of temperature may cause serious damage to the tractor. Many cooling systems today are designed to operate under pressure. Since a sudden release of pressure may result in scalding of the operator, it is recommended as a safety procedure that the tractor be permitted to cool before the radiator filler cap is removed.

The Oiling System. Of all farm machines, the tractor requires the most careful oiling. Due to the nature of its work and the large amount of friction surface in its bearings and cylinders, the tractor must be properly lubricated with good oil and grease if it is to develop its maximum efficiency and last a normal length of time. No other factor affects the life of a tractor so greatly as does oiling.

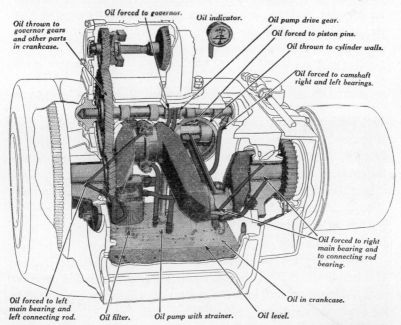

Figure 17—Cross-section of the oiling system showing how all working parts are automatically oiled. Color indicates oil.

Engine lubrication is of special importance, for engine parts are built to fine precision, many parts being held to tolerances as small as one thousandth of an inch. In addition to close tolerances which call for special lubrication, engine parts, moving at high speed, generate considerable heat of friction which must be dissipated or conducted away. Add to the heat of friction, heat generated by combustion and we have a three-fold reason why engine lubrication should be given exacting consideration.

The engine of the tractor shown, is provided with a positive-driven, gear-type oil pump which forces oil under pressure through the replaceable oil filter element, into the main bearings and through the drilled crankshaft to the connecting rod bearings, then through holes in connecting rods to piston pins, see Fig. 17. The crankcase of the tractor illustrated is completely ventilated automatically by clean air drawn through the air cleaner and circulated through the crankcase. Gases are drawn into the combustion chamber where they are burned and expelled through the exhaust.

When the engine is started, the oil indicator (see Fig. 17) will show pressure if the oiling system is working properly. If it does not show pressure, the operator should check the supply of oil in the crankcase. If the oil level is correct, the trouble may be in the oil strainer screen or in the pressure relief valve. Another possibility is that the oil gauge itself may not be functioning properly in which case the gauge should be checked with a master gauge in your dealer's service shop. To insure lubrication, the indicator must show pressure when engine is running.

After every ten hours of operation, the level of oil in the crankcase should be checked and fresh oil added if necessary. After every 120 hours of operation, the crankcase should be drained completely and refilled with fresh oil of proper weight or viscosity for the temperature range in which the tractor will be called upon to operate. (See Fig. 18.)

At the time the crankcase oil is replaced or changed, the replaceable filter element should be removed and a new element installed. The importance of the filter cannot be overestimated. The modern tractor engine, built to close tolerances as mentioned previously, can be seriously damaged by grit particles as small as one-thousandth of an inch. For this reason, the filter element is designed to remove these tiny particles, but when the filter element becomes clogged with grit, it cannot permit the further passage of oil. Grit-laden oil, then, is by-passed through the pressure relief valve to the bearings, pistons, rings, and other precision parts.

A mistaken idea, prevalent among some tractor operators, that **clear** oil is **clean** oil has resulted in serious damage to many a fine tractor engine. Here is a test that you can make in the classroom or at home: fill a test tube with clear oil; add a tea-spoonful of clean sand; shake the tube. The oil remains clear, the grit will settle, but the clear oil is laden with abrasive particles which if placed into a crankcase would bring destruction to bearings in a short time. The same test proves the fallacy of the idea that if oil "feels" good, it is safe oil for the crankcase, for when the engine is stopped, the heavy grit particles settle to the bottom far from the check cock and out of reach of the dip stick.

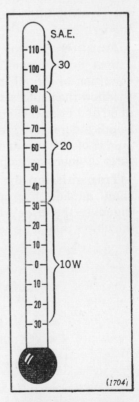

Figure 18—Chart Indicating Correct Weights of Oil to Use at Various Outdoor Temperatures.

Clear oil is not always **clean** oil; likewise **dark** or **black** oil is not necessarily **dirty** oil. When oil becomes dark or discolored in service, the discoloration is due primarily to the entry of soft carbon which in itself is a lubricant.

The present day heavy-duty oils are proof of the point established in the preceding paragraph. The modern heavy-duty oils enter the crankcase just as clear as the regular type oils yet upon draining, they will be discolored; in many cases, actually black. These oils have the faculty for carrying particles in suspension to be drained out with the used oil rather than to drop into the crankcase to foul the clean oil replacing it.

From the foregoing paragraphs it is obvious that we cannot depend upon our eyes or our fingers to judge the condition of the oil; therefore, it is the part of true wisdom to follow the manufacturer's instructions for periodic changes of oil and filter elements. When replacement of filter element is indicated, it is of greatest importance that the replacement unit is of the size and type recommended by the manufacturer of your particular tractor.

Transmission System. The transmission system, as its name implies, transmits or delivers the power from the engine to the drive wheels where it is used to pull loads; to the power take-off where it is available to operate equipment

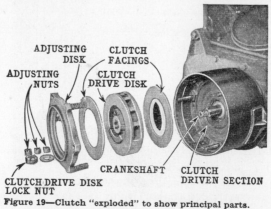

ADJUSTING DISK   CLUTCH FACINGS

ADJUSTING NUTS   CLUTCH DRIVE DISK

CRANKSHAFT   CLUTCH DRIVEN SECTION

CLUTCH DRIVE DISK LOCK NUT

Figure 19—Clutch "exploded" to show principal parts.

requiring power in addition to that necessary for forward travel; and to the power lift, where it is used in raising and lowering integral equipment and, with remote cylinder, for raising, lowering, and adjusting drawn equipment. Power is transmitted to the belt pulley direct.

Power is transmitted from the engine to the drawbar through the clutch and transmission gears and through the final drive or differential to the splined axles. Sliding pinions of varying sizes provide for various tractor speeds forward and one speed in reverse. Any of these sliding pinions is moved into mesh with its respective gear that forms a part of the differential.

A differential is a compensating gear unit that acts so as to transmit power to each of the drive wheels as the tractor turns a corner. It permits one drive wheel to travel faster than the other when turning or when working in rough conditions.

The sole purpose of the clutch (Fig. 19) is to link or connect the power of the engine to the transmission from

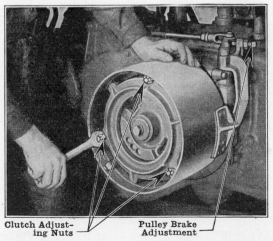

Clutch Adjust-   Pulley Brake
ing Nuts   Adjustment

Figure 20—The clutch is adjusted properly when all nuts are drawn up to even tension.

which it is available for use on the drawbar, belt pulley, power take-off, and power lift. Without such a link no provision could be made for transmission of power to the various power outlets or for changing speeds or direction of travel. To function properly, the clutch should engage smoothly, picking up the load gradually rather than with a jerk.

The clutch is properly adjusted when the nuts are drawn up exactly to the same tension, and the clutch operates with a snap, requiring some pressure to lock it. If it is necessary to tighten the clutch, each nut must be turned down to the same tension, disregarding the number of exposed threads. (See Fig. 20.)

To replace clutch facings, remove dust cover and clutch adjusting disk. (See Fig. 19.)

When installing new clutch facings, make certain that the inside or first clutch facing is in proper position while clutch drive disk is being replaced. Install second clutch facing in clutch adjusting disk, making sure to have the three short springs in place. Adjust clutch as described above.

The transmission and differential units require little attention other than to efficient lubrication which is highly important.

In the enclosed transmission and differential, gears, shafts, and bearings operate in a bath of heavy oil. For proper lubrication of these parts, the correct oil level should be maintained. Periodic check, following the manufacturer's instructions, will determine when oil should be added. Seasonal change in weight of oil used in transmission and differential, in line with the manufacturer's instructions, is necessary for efficient operation and long life. The heavy gears in transmission and differential depend upon a cushion of oil to relieve the tremendous shock of starting and the constant pressure of working under load. Too thin or light an oil will be "squeezed" out by the teeth; too heavy an oil will not be carried around by the gears. A simple test to prove this point is to run a cold gear over a heavy grease—note that the gear simply makes a print or track in the grease without picking it up.

In addition to the engine, transmission, and differential units, there are several oil fittings that require regular attention with a high-pressure grease gun. A thoroughly-lubricated tractor will last longer and give better service than one that is given only ordinary care.

Lubrication and adjustment of front wheel bearings should be given special attention. While the front wheels on most tractors are lubricated by means of a high-pressure fitting, it is advisable to remove the wheels for occasional servicing.

Figure 21—"Exploded" view of front wheel bearing showing relation of parts.

To service front wheel, remove the wheel, take out all old grease, examine the bearings (Fig. 21), clean the two felt washers in gasoline, resoaking in transmission oil before replacing. If these washers are worn thin, replace with new ones. Pack hub and bearing with grease, replace wheel on spindle, and adjust as follows: relieve bearings of all weight by running one wheel up on a block or plank to raise the other. Turn adjusting nut tight; then, back off the adjusting nut 1/3 to 1/2 turn. Adjust opposite wheel in same manner. Wheels should rotate freely but without end-play. Lock adjusting nut at proper point.

Differential Brakes. The differential brakes, one for each drive wheel, are provided to facilitate turning when working in row crops, to stop the tractor, and to hold the tractor stationary on belt work. In operation several cautions should be used in applying differential brakes: when traveling at high speed as on highways or in going to and from fields, brakes should be applied uniformly to both wheels to prevent skidding of the tractor and in extreme cases, upsetting. Never brake one wheel when turning at high speed. Observe, always, that brakes are provided solely for the purposes outlined above.

Differential brakes require only occasional adjustment which should be made in accordance to instructions given in manufacturer's service manual or instruction book.

Power-Shaft Attachment. A power-shaft attachment is a third means of taking power from the tractor engine to drive such machinery as the combine, hay-press, and corn picker. It drives the entire mechanism of this type of machine, the wheels acting merely as supporting or carrying members.

The attachment consists mainly of a shaft, extending back from the tractor, that is driven by the regular transmission. It is especially advantageous in fields where traction conditions make it difficult for the bull or drive wheel of a machine to develop enough power to drive its mechanism.

Hitch and power take-off location of all general-purpose tractors are now standardized so that tractor-drawn equipment, powered through the take-off, is readily interchangeable, thereby saving the operator considerable time and labor in shifting from one machine to another. It is wise, therefore, when buying new equipment for use with older tractors which do not have standardized hitch and power take-off, to convert the tractor to standard rather than to buy the new equipment with parts to adapt it to the old tractor. In this way, your power equipment will be adapted to your present tractor and to the new tractor you may acquire later. Your implement dealer will offer further information at the time you purchase equipment.

Power-Lift Attachment. The power-lift attachment, which supplies power for raising and lowering integral working equipment and, with remote cylinder, for making field adjustments of drawn equipment, is of the hydraulic type, the pump of which is driven from the power shaft. The principles of its design and construction will be considered more fully in the following chapter.

Starting and Lighting Equipment. This equipment, more and more widely used on modern tractors, requires but a small amount of attention, but it is highly important that what servicing is required should be done at periodic intervals if the system is to function properly and dependably.

Starting and lighting equipment includes three important units: the storage battery, which furnishes power for operating the starting motor and the lights; the generator, which develops the energy to be stored in the battery; and the starting motor, which is called upon to "turn over" or crank the tractor engine.

Each of these units requires a certain amount of servicing at periodic intervals. The specific gravity of the battery should be checked weekly, and the solution, or electrolyte, should be replenished with any water you would feel safe in drinking. Generator output or charging rate should be regulated to the demand made upon the battery for starting and lighting. If you operate your tractor without the use of the lights or use them only occasionally, the generator charging rate should be adjusted to approximately 2 ampere charge on the ammeter located on instrument panel. If during busy seasons you operate all night, the charge rate must be set so ammeter shows a 4-1/2 ampere charge. To change charging rate, remove the generator dust band and loosen the brush holder screw. Move the brush in direction armature rotates

to increase, and move in opposite direction to decrease.
After obtaining desired charging rate, tighten the brush
holding screw. Replace the cover band, making sure it is
tight and covers the openings properly.

All connections in the entire system should be kept clean
and snug-fitting. When your new tractor is delivered with
starting and lighting equipment, it is advisable to check carefully the instructions covering this equipment to familiarize
yourself with the servicing required.

Maintenance of Rubber Tires. The broad use of rubber
tires on farm tractors and machinery has resulted in a great
saving both in time and operating cost. There are, however,
certain basic funda-
mentals in the care of
tires that should be
followed carefully if
the owner is to derive
maximum benefit from
his investment. First
and most important is
to maintain proper

Figure 22—Proper inflation is of utmost importance in the life of rubber tires.

pressure for the work at hand. Your best guide to proper inflation is the instruction book covering the particular tractor
or implement under consideration. Read your instruction
book or consult your dealer concerning proper inflation, and
check air pressure regularly. Underinflated tires suffer
from rim bruises, sidewall snagging, and carcass failure.
Overinflation increases tread wear (on tractors and ground-
driven implements) and because of reduced traction, weakens
the carcass, and hastens weather checking. An air pressure
gauge and a good tire pump are essential in maintaining
proper inflation. Proper inflation is especially important
where fluid weight is used since the air space is greatly reduced. (See Fig. 22.) A special air-water gauge should be used
for testing tires carrying fluid weight.

Grease and oil are natural enemies of rubber. Protect tires

from oil and grease as much as possible. Should tires become spattered with oil or grease, wipe them off with a rag dampened with gasoline—but do this job *outside* the implement shed to reduce fire hazard. Never allow tires to stand in barnyard acids. If spray chemical gets on the tires, wash it off.

Inspect tires periodically for carcass breaks and cuts and have them repaired immediately. No cut is too small to require attention, for if it is not repaired, further damage will result.

Use tractor wheel weights (according to manufacturer's instructions) to secure maximum traction and minimum slippage.

Avoid high transporting speeds. Implement tires, unless otherwise specified, are not designed for speeds exceeding fifteen miles an hour. Take added precautions as tires age.

Don't overload. This applies particularly to combine grain tank extensions. Reduce speed and load, if possible, on rough ground.

Protect from sunlight the tires of idle implements.

When a rubber-tired implement is to be idle for a considerable time, block up the axles to take the weight off the tires, but leave the tires inflated.

Questions

1. *What changes have been brought about on the farm by the more general use of tractors?*

2. *What is an internal-combustion engine?*

3. *What is the difference between a two-stroke cycle engine and a four-stroke cycle engine? What are the four strokes of the latter?*

4. *What three elements are required for efficient engine operation?*

5. *What parts make up the fuel system; how would you check each part?*

6. *What is the importance of the air cleaner; how is it serviced?*

7. *Describe the function of the magneto; how would you check it for operating efficiency?*

8. *Describe a step by step check of the ignition system.*

9. *How does the oiling system of the tractor illustrated operate? Why is an oil filter of special importance in the modern tractor?*

10. *What is the function of the valves?*

11. *Why is the cooling system necessary? What attention does it require?*

12. *Describe the transmission of power from engine to drive wheels; belt pulley; power take-off; and power lift.*

13. *What is a differential unit? Describe a clutch.*

14. *What are the advantages of a power-shaft attachment?*

15. *What per cent of farms in your community have tractors, and what per cent should have them?*

16. *Mention several of the important points in proper care of pneumatic tires.*

General-Purpose Tractors

Modern farm tractors may be divided into two general classes: the general-purpose type and the standard type. While the standard type tractor is of earlier design, the general-purpose type has come into such universal favor that it will be given first discussion in this text.

The general-purpose type of tractor, as its name implies, furnishes power for practically all farm work. Not only does it perform all the drawbar, belt, and power shaft jobs but, with the wide variety of integral equipment available for it, the general-purpose tractor puts speed and economy into many jobs for which the standard type tractor cannot be adapted, such as the cultivating of row-crops.

Taking into account the size of farms, the nature and relative importance of the various jobs to be done, manufacturers of present-day tractors aim to meet the need of every farm both in the matter of power required and type

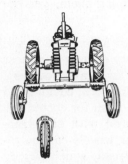

of equipment to be used for the crops to be grown. As a result, there is today a wide range of power sizes and types of general-purpose tractors to meet practically all requirements. In addition to the type in general use, there are variations of the general-purpose tractor adapted to special work, such as the tractor shown in Figure 23, which is available with adjustable front axle for use in extremely soft ground and with interchangeable single front wheel

Figure 23—General-purpose tractor—with adjustable front axle which is interchangeable with single front wheel shown.

for use in garden crops where rows are extremely narrow.

The smaller general-purpose tractor, of four-wheel type, Figure 24, is built especially to bring all the advantages of power farming to the smaller farm and to serve as auxiliary or "helper" power on the large farm. Available for this tractor is a complete line of integral equipment, easily and quickly attached and detached and controlled by the hydraulic power control system.

In heavier soils and on larger farms where row-crops are raised, the general-purpose tractor of three-plow power fills the need for a tractor adaptable to the varied operations in plowing, planting, cultivating, and harvesting, in addition to belt work.

Weight Is Factor. A general-purpose tractor must be heavy enough to give good traction efficiency in plowing and similar heavy work, yet no heavier than needed, because a larger part of its work is on mellow soil. Similarly, its engine must have enough power for the heavier drawbar jobs, yet be efficient at lighter loads. The clearance of all parts that pass above cultivated plants must be sufficient to allow tractor to pass over them without harming them, yet the machine must not be top-heavy.

A typical general-purpose tractor with adjustable tread, which can be equipped for a wide variety of uses in almost any row-crop is illustrated in Fig. 5. Two- and four-row planters, two- and four-row cultivators for corn, cotton, and other crops, and two- and four-row bedders for cotton are some of the equipment that can be used with this tractor. For such jobs as plowing, the rear wheels can be reversed right to left and set in 56-inch tread, which largely overcomes side draft. Fig. 25 shows the four-row cultivating unit attached to the adjustable tread tractor. Front wheels of many general-purpose tractors may be reversed as shown

Figure 24—The small general-purpose tractor with integral mold-board plow

Figure 25—Cultivating cotton four rows at a time with an adjustable tread tractor.

in Fig. 27 to provide easier steering control, especially in listed crop territories where it is necessary to keep the front wheels on the ridges. This extra clearance is an advantage in exceptionally muddy conditions since mud will not accumulate under the frame. In normal conditions, steering

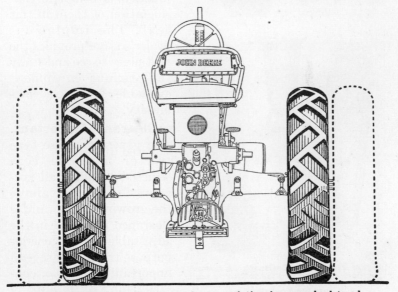

Figure 26—Diagram showing maximum variation in rear wheel tread.

is easiest with the wheels in narrow setting. Another important aid to easy steering, operator comfort and safety, and increased tire life is the load equalizer (Fig. 28) which equalizes the front end load over both wheels, permitting the tractor to "walk over" surface irregularities and to conform with ridges in the field.

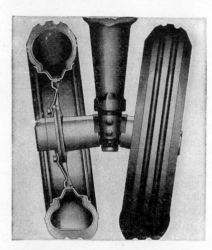

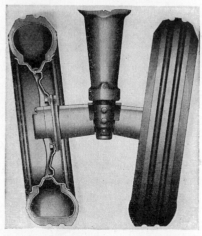

Manufacturers of tractors and farm equipment now provide a wide variety of equipment for their tractors, making it possible to grow and harvest practically any crop, using tractor power exclusively. The attachments and machines available are so numerous as to make impractical a complete consideration of them in this text. The implement dealer's store provides the best place to see and study the various equipment available for each community.

Clearance Important. The general-purpose type tractor must be constructed to allow all necessary clearance above the growing crops. Ample clearance is gained in the adjustable tread general-purpose tractor by several important features of construction. By mounting

Figure 27—Front wheels set in normal position (top) and in wide setting as used on listed ridges or for easier steering in muddy conditions.

the front of the tractor on a single support and extending rear wheel tread to straddle two rows, the engine is placed between the rows. In addition, the high drive wheels, in combination with the properly-designed rear axle housing, provide ample clearance for cultivating all row-crops.

It is highly desirable in planting and cultivating to turn completely around without stopping and be in position to continue back on the next set of rows. To make this possible, there is a separate brake for each rear wheel on the general-purpose tractor shown. Pressing the brake pedal for the inner wheel holds the wheel back and aids the front wheels in swinging the tractor around sharply.

Hydraulic Power Control. To assist further in making turns at ends of rows and to relieve the operator of the work of lifting integral equipment manually, a hydraulic power lift is built for these tractors. Coupled to the power lift, the plow, planter, cultivator, or other integral equipment is raised and lowered by this device. When the control pedal or lever of the power lift is tripped, the working equipment is lifted promptly by engine power. A second touch of the control releases the lift and allows the equipment to drop. An adjustment is provided whereby the operator may control speed of drop for both light and

Figure 28—The front wheel load equalizer is shown here in X-Ray view to show differential construction.

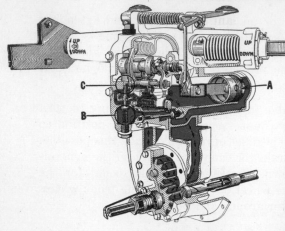

Illustration at left shows the power lift in the lowered position. The piston, "A", is extended and the rocker shafts are rotated so that the implements are in their lowered position. The check valve, "B", is away from the seat and the cylinder type by-pass valve at the top, "C", is also open, permitting the oil to recirculate.

The oil is directed through the throttle valve, "D", onto the head of the piston. The piston starts back, rotating the crank and rocker arms. As the rocker arms approach the raised position, the connecting rod contacts the cam trip pin, "E". In completing the full stroke, this cam trip pin disengages the cam trip lever from the cam, "F", permitting the power lift control shaft to be rotated by the heavy control spring, "G".

The rotation of the control shaft causes the check valve, "B", to close, preventing the return of oil from the head end of the piston. Now the implements will stay in the raised position. Notice, too, that the by-pass valve is now opened, permitting the pumped oil to recirculate under pressure from the pump.

Figure 29—Hydraulic power lift.

To lower the implements, the operator must press down on the foot control pedal. No action will take place until the pedal has traveled the full distance. This cracks the check valve, "B", from the seat and also keeps the by-pass valve, "C", open. The rate at which the implements drop is controlled by the throttle valve, "D". By increasing or decreasing the opening between valve and seat, the rate at which the implement drops is increased or decreased.

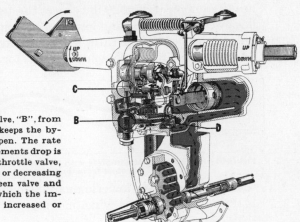

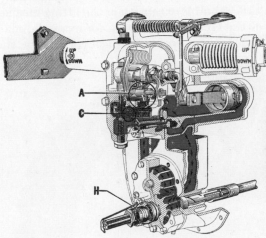

After the implements are removed, disengage the power shaft which drives the pump. It is better to have the rocker shafts in the down position when not in operation, since the tension in the rocker shaft spring is very little. This spring prevents the piston from drifting.

heavy equipment. Fig. 29 illustrates the action of the hydraulic power lift in raising and lowering equipment. Besides being independent of the operator's physical strength, the engine-driven power lift is independent of the forward movement of

Figure 30—Remote cylinder complete with hydraulic hose. Fittings are capped to protect from dust and dirt.

the outfit—lifting or lowering may be done while the tractor is stationary as well as when moving.

When the power lift is equipped for remote cylinder operation (see Figs. 30 and 31) the power of the engine, acting through the hydraulic lift, may be used in adjusting drawn equipment. With this valuable extension of the lifting mechanism, the height of the combine platform, for example, may be varied quickly, easily, and exactly to meet conditions; the

Figure 31—Power lift equipped for remote cylinder operation with hydraulic cylinder connections in position.

plow may be raised just enough to pass over a bad spot in the field; the disk harrow may be straightened to cross a grassed waterway, and angled quickly upon returning to work.

Any degree of variation within the extreme limits set by the operator may be gained, simply by moving the control lever in the selective range, yet, when the lever is moved to either extreme, the maximum lift or drop is reached promptly.

In making the simple change from rockshaft operation to remote cylinder control of drawn equipment, several basic considerations should be remembered. While the piston in the remote cylinder operates on a reciprocal motion, powered on both the outward and inward strokes, the cylinder should be placed so that the lifting load is always applied on the outward stroke, thereby taking advantage of the full area of the piston for the heavier load. In coupling to the tractor, knurled coupling adapter rings should be drawn up snugly by hand only—never with a wrench. Since valve openings, or apertures, are extremely small—many of them smaller than the lead in a fine-line pencil—it is of utmost importance that dirt and other foreign matter are kept out of the system. The manufacturer has provided every protection possible, yet it is the operator's responsibility to use extreme care in keeping the system clean.

The hydraulic unit requires very little servicing other than a periodic check for proper oil level. Approximately every twelve months the entire unit should be drained and refilled to proper level with the correct grade of oil. When storing the remote cylinder, the piston should be pushed all the way into the cylinder to protect the polished shaft from exposure to dust and moisture.

Forward Speeds. In a general-purpose tractor, flexibility of speed has much to do with capacity and efficiency. In cultivating, especially, there are times when it is desired to go very slowly. At other times, both speed and effectiveness are gained by traveling fast and throwing the soil briskly. To meet this wide range of speed demands, it is

Figure 32—Cultivating with a general-purpose tractor and integral
vegetable cultivator.

usual to provide several forward speeds in the transmission gears. These speeds in the general-purpose tractors used for our example range from a slow speed of approximately 1-1/2 miles per hour to high speeds as fast as 12-1/2 miles per hour. Still further variation in speed may be had by throttling down the engine.

The power take-off device, which supplies power directly by shaft to machines being pulled by the tractor, has found wide application and great usefulness on tractors of both the standard and the general-purpose types.

Care Important. When the general-purpose tractor supplants animal power on the farm, it is doubly important that it be given proper care. If the owner is dependent upon his tractor for all farm jobs, delays are costly. Careful handling, strict attention to oiling, adjusting, and repairing the tractor and the equipment that is used with it will result in greater satisfaction and greater net profits.

The care and operation of the various units attachable to the tractor are discussed in the chapters devoted to each particular type of machine.

Standard Type Tractors

While the general-purpose tractors, described on preceding pages, meet the needs of the row-crop farmer in
plowing, planting, cultivating, and harvesting his crops, the
particular power requirements of the small-grain grower
and the orchardist are best met by tractors of standard design, especially adapted to the work at hand. On larger
farms, where row-crops are grown, standard type tractors
are often used to supplement the general-purpose tractors
in preparing seedbeds and harvesting the crops.

What has been said about the design and care of the
general-purpose tractors applies so generally to the standard
types that a further discussion is unnecessary.

The standard type tractor, furnishing power at three
outlets, the drawbar, belt, and power take-off, is used for
practically all power requirements except planting and
cultivating. The tractor, shown in Fig. 33, is a typical

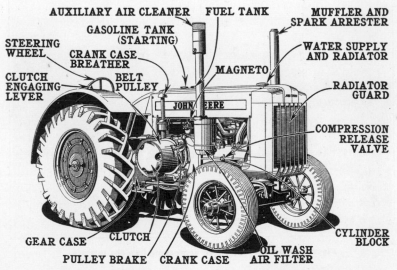

Figure 33—Standard type tractor of three-four-plow power.

three-four-plow tractor of this type. For smaller farms, a standard type tractor of two-plow power, shown in Fig. 34 is available. A further variation of the standard type is the orchard tractor, a tractor of two-plow power, built low and compact, and with wheels and pulley shielded to facilitate operation under low-hanging limbs in orchards. Fig. 35 shows an orchard tractor at work in an orange grove.

Figure 34—A standard type tractor of two-plow power.

Figure 35—Orchard type tractor working in a citrus grove.

Questions

1. *Name and describe two types of tractors.*

2. *Tell some of the advantages of the general-purpose tractor.*

3. *Why is weight an important factor in the general-purpose type of tractor?*

4. *What are the main differences in construction between the general-purpose type and the standard type of tractor?*

5. *What are the advantages of a power lift on a general-purpose tractor? Describe the principle of its operation.*

6. *How does the remote cylinder increase the usefulness of the power lift? What servicing does it require?*

7. *Of what use are the wheel, or differential, brakes on the tractor?*

8. *Why is variation of speed a valuable asset in a tractor of this type?*

9. *What are the important advantages of the standard type tractor?*

10. *Review the more important points in the care of tractors.*

Part Two
PREPARATION OF THE SEEDBED

BEFORE discussing the implements used in preparing the soil for planting, it is well to consider, briefly, the results sought by their use. A clear understanding of the purpose and value of the machine studied is necessary before details of its operation and care can be fully appreciated. Thus, the reasons for certain adjustments on a plow become quite evident when we know that the basic purpose of plowing is to pulverize the soil and cover field trash.

The Ideal Seedbed. It is unwise to say that any one type of seedbed is desirable for all crops and all soils. The make-up and process of preparing what might be called a good seedbed in gumbo soil would differ greatly from that used in sandy soil.

In general, the seedbed should be roomy, thoroughly pulverized, and compact. It should have perfect contact with the subsoil to facilitate the rise of moisture. Large air spaces, bunches of field trash, and hard lumps or clods are undesirable, as their presence retards root growth and breaks the contact with the subsoil. The operations and the equipment employed in preparing a seedbed will vary with soil and field conditions and the results wanted.

Tillage Equipment. Implements used in preparing good seedbeds vary widely depending upon soil, territory, and crop to be planted. The moldboard plow is by far the most universally used, although the disk tiller, disk plow, field cultivator, or tool-bar cultivator, and the disk harrow are important tools in seedbed preparation.

The Plow. The purpose of the plow is to pulverize or break up the soil, admitting air and light, and to cover surface trash or manure deeply and completely to be mixed with the soil to decay and release plant food to the subsequent crop. Under conditions where surface trash must be covered completely to control such pests as the European Corn Borer, the moldboard plow, equipped with trash control aids, stands at the head of the list of seedbed-making tools.

The disk tiller, or one-way disk, was introduced originally in the Great Plains, where its big capacity speeded seedbed preparation and where its faculty for binding stubble to the surface soil made its use advisable as a soil and moisture conserving practice. The field of its effective usefulness has broadened to the extent that it is used to some degree in practically all parts of the country.

The disk plow which depends upon a rolling cutting action to cut and turn soil is used primarily in sticky, waxy land where a moldboard plow encounters "shedding" or "scouring" difficulties, and in hard, dry, or stony ground where it is difficult to gain penetration with a moldboard plow.

The Disk Harrow is a valuable implement when used before and after plowing, or when used alone in preparing seedbeds for some crops. It pulverizes clods, mixes trash with the soil, and forms a mulch when used before plowing. When used after plowing, it chops lumps, closes air spaces, and makes the seedbed compact.

Spike- and Spring-Tooth Harrows. Finishing the seedbed and destroying weeds before and after planting are the main purposes of spike- and spring-tooth harrows. Their crushing and stirring effect breaks up clods and crusted topsoil, leaving a fine surface mulch for planting or for plant growth.

Soil Pulverizer or Packer. The pulverizer, or packer as it is more commonly called, crushes lumps, closes air spaces, and leaves the seedbed firm, in ideal condition for planting. The packer is used extensively in territories where the soil tends to blow. It leaves an irregular, firm surface which does not blow so readily as a looser, more regular surface.

Chapter II.

PLOWS

Plow Bottoms

Importance of the Bottoms. A plow is no better than its bottoms. No matter how well the frame may be built, how modern its design, the plow will be only as satisfactory as its bottoms. If the bottoms fail to scour and turn the soil properly, the seedbed will be uneven and lumpy, resulting in lower yields. If the bottoms turn an even furrow, cover trash well, and pulverize the furrow slice as desired, a uniform seedbed will result.

Costly delays at plowing time are often caused by plow bottoms that refuse to scour. The trouble may be in the way the bottoms are made. It may be in the adjustment of the hitch, it may be due to dull or improperly-set shares, or to looseness or misalignment of the bottoms on the standards. The plowman must be constantly on the alert for signs of inefficiency in his plow bottoms.

Parts of the Bottom. The plow bottom consists of share, landside, moldboard, and frog (Fig. 36). The share and landside act as a wedge in the soil, cutting the furrow loose from the subsoil much as a wedge splits a log. The curved surface of the upper part of the share and the properly-curved

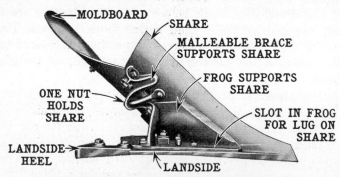

Figure 36—Plow Bottom with parts named.

moldboard act as a single curve to invert the furrow slice. In passing over this curved surface, the furrow is twisted and broken, and the soil is pulverized, mixed, and aerated.

The steel frog holds the bottom parts together. The landside and moldboard are bolted solidly to the frog, while the share, on most bottoms, is made quickly detachable to facilitate share changes. To remove or replace the share on the bottom shown in Fig. 36, it is necessary to loosen but one nut; this quick-detachable feature saves time when shares are removed for sharpening.

Certain types of chilled-iron plows have a detachable chilled shin-piece that serves as a long-wearing cutting edge for the shin of the moldboard where the hardest wear occurs (Fig. 37).

Types of Bottoms. Different types of soil require bottoms of different shapes to accomplish the results desired in plowing. The texture of the soil and the amount of moisture it contains, determine whether it should be pulverized thoroughly or merely turned over, to be pulverized with other implements. A mellow loam soil and soils of similar texture should be plowed with a bottom that will pulverize well, while a sticky, wet clay soil should be plowed with a bottom that will break it as little as possible, leaving the pulverizing to be done with other implements.

Figure 37—Chilled-iron bottom with detachable shin-piece.

The pulverizing effect of a plow depends upon the shape of its bottom. A bottom with a long, gradual curve in the moldboard turns the furrow slice gently and disturbs its composition but little. The other extreme is the short, abruptly curved moldboard that twists and shears the soil as it passes over it, making a mellow, well-pulverized furrow. The pulver-

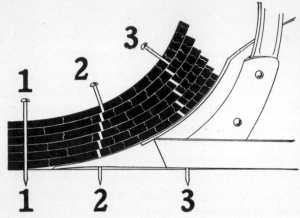

Figure 38—Principle of the pulverizing effect of the plow bottom under most soil conditions. The shearing effect produced by the curved surface is illustrated by pins 1, 2, and 3. Pin 1 is sheared into many parts when it reaches position of pin 3. Bending the pages at the corner of a book will illustrate this principle. The breaking effect produced by the curved surface is also illustrated.

izing effect produced by the curved surface of the moldboard is illustrated in Fig. 38.

Between these two extremes are many types of bottoms designed to meet many different soil conditions, but for general use, bottoms may be classified as breaker, stubble, general purpose, slat moldboard, and blackland. The breaker (Fig. 39) is used in tough sod where complete turning of the furrow slice without materially disturbing its texture is desired. Stubble bottoms (Fig. 40) are especially adapted to plowing in old ground where good pulverizing of the soil is desired. General purpose bottoms (Fig. 41) meet the demand for bottoms that will do good work in stubble, tame sod, old ground, and a variety of similar conditions. The general purpose bottom is de-

Figure 39—Breaker bottom.

Figure 40—Stubble bottom.

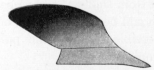

Figure 41—General purpose bottom.

Figure 42—Slat moldboard bottom.

Figure 43—Blackland bottom.

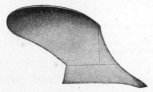

Figure 44—Deep tillage bottom.

signed to do satisfactory work in the varying conditions found on the average farm.

The slat moldboard bottom (Fig. 42) is used in loose, sticky soils, and the blackland bottom (Fig. 43) in gumbo and "buckshot" soils. In both types of soil, scouring is a serious problem.

The deep tillage bottom (Fig. 44) is used in certain restricted territories where it is desirable to plow to unusually great depths—as deep as sixteen inches.

There are a number of variations of these general bottom shapes built to meet a wide variety of soil conditions but, in every case, the manufacturer provides the implement dealer with the types of bottoms suited to his territory.

Materials Used in Bottoms. Classified according to materials used in manufacture, there are two kinds of plow bottoms—steel and chilled cast-iron. Steel bottoms may be either solid steel or hardened soft-center steel. The latter bottoms are in more general use. In some sections, the soil conditions are such that a combination of chilled-iron shares and soft-center steel moldboards is used with excellent results. Both steel and chilled bottoms are used by some farmers who have varying soil conditions on their farms.

Soft-Center Steel Bottoms. A very highly polished fine-textured steel moldboard is necessary to good scouring in sticky, fine-grained soils. Soft-center steel has the necessary hardness and thickness for good scouring and long wear on the outer surfaces, and

Figure 45—Genuine soft-center steel. Nos. 1 and 3 are layers of high-carbon steel, harder than that commonly known as "tool steel". No. 2 is a layer of soft, tough steel, the hard steel having been fused to it. Note uniform thickness of layers.

strength enough in
the inner layer to
withstand shocks
and heavy loads in
difficult soils. The
outside layers are
very high in carbon,
extremely hard,
dense steel. Be-
tween these two

Figure 46—Genuine soft-center steel share point.
A—Patches of hard tool steel. 1 and 3—Hard steel.
2—Soft steel. 4—Steel landside, lap-welded. Note
thickness of hard-steel layers.

hard layers is a layer of soft, tough steel, the hard steel
having been fused to it (Fig. 45). In genuine soft-center steel,
all three layers are uniformly thick. There is no outcropping
of soft spots, no thin places in the outer layers to wear through
rapidly. Fig. 46 shows cross-section of a genuine soft-center
steel share point, illustrating how the top and bottom of the
point are armored for longer wear by wear-resisting plates
of tool steel.

Solid Steel Bottoms. Bottoms made of solid steel,
untempered, are used in soils where scouring as a rule is not
difficult. They should not be used in sandy or gravelly

soil, as they wear too
rapidly under these conditions. Solid steel shares are
sometimes used with soft-
center steel moldboards
where soil conditions do
not require the more costly soft-center steel shares
for scouring.

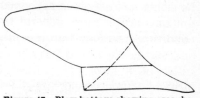

Figure 47—Plow bottom showing area, below dotted line, which receives 75 percent
of the draft when plowing, illustrating the
necessity of keeping shares sharp for light
draft of the plow.

Chilled-Iron Bottoms.
Plow bottoms made of
chilled iron are designed
primarily for use in sandy
or gravelly soil where the
share and moldboard must
withstand the scratching

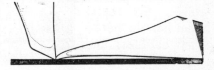

Figure 48—Heavy lines show proper shape
of sharp share points for good penetration.
Dotted lines show how worn points look
before sharpening.

and hard wear of soil of this type, and where the denser, finer-grained surface of more costly soft-center steel is not necessary for scouring. The material used in these bottoms is extremely hard and long wearing due to a process called "chilling".

In casting chilled shares, a piece of metal called a "chiller" is placed into the mold along the cutting edge and point where the finished share is to be chilled. When the hot metal comes into contact with the "chiller", the sudden cooling leaves the grain of the metal at right angles to the surface. Thus, the dirt rubs the ends of the grain in the metal when passing over the share. A smooth and long-wearing surface results. Chilled shares may be sharpened by grinding but, because of their low cost, it is usually more satisfactory to replace worn shares with new ones.

Sharpening Plowshares. The share is the most vital part of the bottom. It is the "business end"—the pioneer part in all of the work that a plow does. Draft, penetration, steady-running, and good work all depend upon the share.

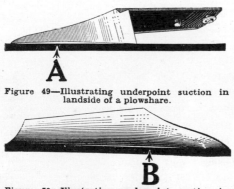

Figure 49—Illustrating underpoint suction in landside of a plowshare.

Figure 50—Illustrating underpoint suction in throat of a plowshare.

Note Fig. 47 which shows the area of the plow bottom that is responsible for 75 percent of the draft when the plow is at work. This illustration shows clearly the importance of keeping the share in good cutting condition at all times. Note, also, Fig. 48. A dull share may cause poor penetration and may greatly increase the draft of a plow. A sharp, correctly-set share adds to the efficiency and good work of the plow bottom.

Many farmers have shop equipment for sharpening their plowshares, while the great majority depend upon local blacksmiths or mechanics for this service. In either case, it is well to know how shares should be sharpened.

When sharpening soft-center or solid-steel shares, the point of the share should be heated to a low, cherry red (not too hot) and hammered on the top side until the point is sharp. Hammering should be done at a cherry red only, since working the share at a high heat destroys the quality of the steel. The entire cutting edge should be drawn from the underside until sharp. Only as much as can be hammered should be heated at one time. The body of the share should not be heated while sharpening, but should remain cool to prevent warping and disturbing of the fitted edges.

Should the share get out of shape or the fitted edges become warped during the sharpening process, the entire blade should be restored to proper shape before hardening. This can be done best at a black heat.

Soft-center steel shares should be hardened after sharpen-

Figure 51—Bottoms are the "business end" of the plow, for no plow is better than its bottoms.

ing. To do a thorough job of hardening, it is necessary to prepare the fire to heat the entire share uniformly to a cherry
red. Care should be used in getting the heat uniform. The
share should be taken from the fire and dipped into a tub
of clean, cold water with the cutting edge down. Care should
be taken to keep the blade in a perpendicular position during
this process.

Solid steel shares should not be hardened.

Setting Shares for Suction. The plow bottom is led
into the ground and held to its work by the underpoint
suction of the share. Such suction is produced by turning
the point of the share down slightly below the level of the
underside of the share (see Fig. 49). The amount of suc-

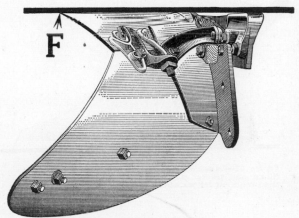

Figure 52—Riding and tractor plows do not require
wing bearing at "F".

tion necessary depends upon the type of plow and existing
soil conditions. Plows to be used in stiff clay soils which are
harder to penetrate than light loam soils, require more
suction in the share point.

Landside suction (see Fig. 53) in a plowshare holds the
bottom to its full-width cut and is produced by turning the

point of the share toward the unplowed ground. The land suction, as well as the down suction, should be measured when the share is new, so that the same amount of suck can be given the share when it is sharpened.

The importance of having the correct amount of suck in the share cannot be emphasized too strongly. Too little underpoint suction will cause the plow to "ride out" of the ground and cut a furrow of uneven depth. Too much will cause "bobbing" and heavy draft. In either case, the plow will not operate smoothly. If the landside suction is too great, the bottom tends to cut a wider furrow than can be handled properly, and the reverse is true when the landside suction is not sufficient.

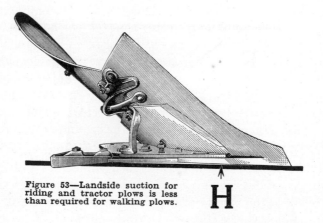

Figure 53—Landside suction for riding and tractor plows is less than required for walking plows.

H

To secure proper suction, set the point of the share down until there is 1/8- to 3/16-inch suction under the landside at point "A" (Fig. 49). See that clearance in throat of share at "B" (Fig. 50) is at least 1/8-inch. Set edge of share at wing point "F", without wing bearing (Fig. 52). For landside, set should be about 3/16-inch clearance at "H" (Fig. 53).

Care of the Bottom. The plow bottom will give the best satisfaction when given the best care. If kept in good condition, it will give little scouring trouble. If permitted to rust, it may cause any amount of hard work and lost time.

One of the first rules a plowman should learn is to keep the bright surfaces of his plow bottoms well polished and to apply a light coating of oil whenever the plow is not in use. Strict observance of this rule will save many hours of difficulty in getting a rusted surface repolished. A heavy coating of a good, hard oil or good rust preventive should be applied to the bottoms when storing the plow from season to season.

Plow manufacturers paint or varnish the surfaces of new plow bottoms to protect them from moisture from factory to user. This protective coating must be removed before the plow is taken into the field. This can be accomplished best by means of a paint and varnish remover which is obtainable at most paint stores. A can of concentrated lye dissolved in two or three quarts of water will serve the same purpose. The solution should be applied with a swab or a piece of gunny sack, the operator being careful not to get it on his hands. After the coating has been softened in this manner, it can be scraped off readily with a putty knife or similar instrument, care being taken not to scratch the polished surface.

If the new plow is not to be used immediately after this protective covering has been removed, the bottoms should be oiled, as the metal rusts readily if exposed to the air after treatment with the suggested strong solutions.

In case a plow bottom becomes badly rusted, working it in a coarse sandy or gravelly soil will aid in restoring a land polish or if too badly pitted it may be necessary to have it reground at the factory.

Rolling Coulter and Jointer. One of the most important duties of the plow is to cover the stubble, stalks, or other trash usually found on the surface of a field. Thorough covering of such matter hurries its decomposition and makes cultivation of future crops less difficult than when trash is left on top of the seedbed to clog cultivating machines. Complete covering of surface trash is an absolute necessity where plowing is intended to control the spread of such pests as the European Corn Borer.

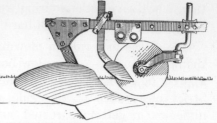

Figure 54—Rolling coulter and independent jointer properly adjusted for good work.

The rolling coulter and jointer attachments for moldboard plows have proved to be big aids to clean plowing and good covering. Their value has grown in importance with the advent of high-powered, high-speed tractors. At higher plowing speeds the work of the rolling coulter and independent jointer (Fig. 54) is indispensable in maintaining perfect plowing performance. The rolling coulter cuts through the surface trash and aids in securing a clean furrow wall, reducing the draft on the cutting edge of the plow bottom. In reality, the jointer is a miniature

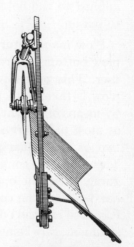

Figure 55—When used alone, the coulter should be set 1/2- to 5/8-inch to the land, and the hub should be about 3 inches to rear of the share point.

plow, the purpose of which is to cut a small furrow off the main furrow slice and throw it toward the furrow in such a manner that all stubble and trash are buried in the bottom of the furrow.

For best results, the hub of the coulter should be set about one-inch back of the share point with the blade running just deep enough to cut the trash, about three to four inches in ordinary conditions. The jointer should cut about two inches deep. There should be about 1/8-inch space between the jointer and the coulter blade.

When the rolling coulter is used alone, it should be set about 1/2- to 5/8-inch to the land (Fig. 55). The hub of the coulter should be about three inches behind the point of the share. In soil that does not scour well, more pressure on the

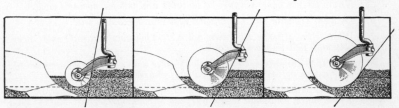

Figure 56—Large rolling coulters mount trash more readily than small ones, thereby insuring a clean-cut furrow with less draft.

moldboard can be secured by setting the coulter farther to land. If there is considerable trash on the field, the coulter should be set just deep enough to cut it—if set too deep, it pushes instead of cuts trash. The larger rolling coulters prove more effective in trashy conditions, as they mount trash more effectively than smaller coulters (see Fig. 56). When

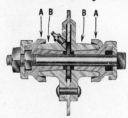

plowing sod, the coulter must be deep enough to cut the roots below the surface, usually about one-inch shallower than the share is cutting.

Many present-day coulters are equipped with adjustable bearings which provide means for taking up wear which may occur. Figure 57 shows a cross-sectional view of this type of coulter bearing. When a

Figure 57—Cross-sectional view of adjustable rolling coulter bearing with adjustable sleeves indicated at "A" and "B".

small amount of wear develops, adjusting the inner nut will keep the coulter blade running true.

Keeping the rolling coulter sharp and well oiled and the jointer sharp and properly set will add greatly to the efficiency of their work.

Questions

1. Why is a good bottom essential to good plowing?

2. Name the parts of a plow bottom and tell the purpose of each.

3. How is the plowshare removed for sharpening?

4. Describe the relation between shape of moldboard and its pulverizing effect upon the soil.

5. Name the five general types of bottoms and tell purposes of each.

6. In what kinds of soil are chilled cast-iron bottoms used?

7. What is the difference between solid steel bottoms and soft-center steel bottoms? Tell purpose of each.

8. Why is it important to keep plowshares sharp? Describe process of sharpening soft-center and solid steel shares.

9. What is meant by "underpoint suction" and "landside suction" in a plowshare, and what is the purpose of each? Describe results of improper suction and tell how to measure correct set for plowshares.

10. How would you care for plow bottoms when in use and when not in use? How would you remove factory varnish from plow bottoms?

11. Describe purpose and proper adjustment of the rolling coulter and jointer, and mention the advantages of their use.

Tractor Plows

The modern tractor plow is one of the most important items of farming equipment. When we consider the work it does—cutting, lifting, turning and pulverizing tons of soil, burying surface trash deeply and completely—it becomes apparent that time is well spent in acquainting ourselves with its operation, care and adjustment.

In the previous pages we discussed the plow bottom and its importance as the basic part of the plow; here we shall discuss the different types of plows and the adjustments necessary for best operations under varying conditions.

Tractor moldboard plows are built in several types or styles to meet the requirements of farmers in all sections of the country. Tractor drawn plows are available with from one to five bottoms to match the power available on farms of various sizes and to meet plowing conditions. Integral, or tractor-carried plows are built for most general-purpose tractors, while two-way plows, used widely in irrigated

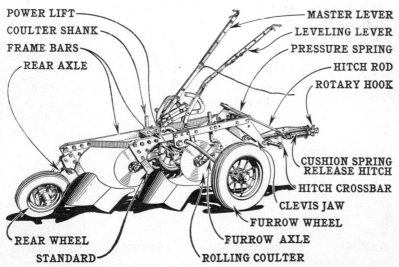

Figure 58—Two-bottom tractor plow with important parts indicated.

regions, hilly farms and, frequently, in plowing on the contour, are available in drawn and integral types. The market gardener, the farmer who has small, irregular fields to plow, and many others who find it an advantage to turn all furrows one way find the two-way especially valuable.

The two-bottom tractor-drawn plow (Fig. 58) is probably the most generally used size and type because of the popularity of the general-purpose tractor of "two-plow" power. Fig. 59 illustrates a larger plow of similar construction, matched to the need of the farmer of larger acreage. Plows of extra heavy-duty construction, designed for deep plowing in the heaviest types of soil, are usually equipped with deep tillage bottoms (Fig. 44) to meet the specific needs for which their greater strength is required.

Fig. 61 illustrates a tractor two-way of the integral or tractor-carried type. Attached to the general-purpose tractor, it becomes a compact unit with the tractor, the power lift of the tractor, operated by the tractor engine, raising and lowering the bottoms. Depth is varied and the plow leveled by means of levers. Gauge wheels hold the plow to maximum depth set.

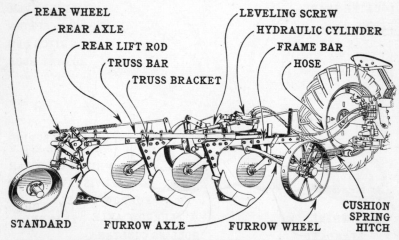

Figure 59—Three-bottom truss-frame plow with principal parts indicated.

A tractor-drawn two-way plow is shown in Fig. 60. Power-lift units (right- and left-hand) raise and lower the bottoms,

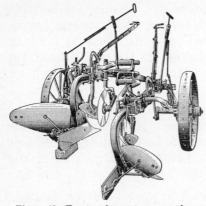

while lever controls provide for depth and leveling adjustments. The two-furrow two-way plow is shown in Fig. 62.

Operation of Plows. The first important consideration in gaining good plowing performance, is the condition of the plow bottoms. Bottoms must be in proper adjustment, shares and rolling coulters must be sharp, wheels

Figure 60—Tractor-drawn two-way plow.

must be properly set, and the plow must be hitched correctly if good work is to be expected.

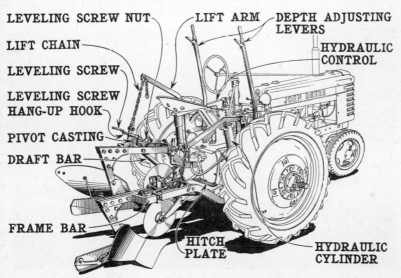

Figure 61—The integral two-way plow with general-purpose tractor.

When a new plow is delivered by the implement dealer, it is usually in proper adjustment for efficient work. If the rear wheel adjustment becomes loose and permits the landside to become lower than the rear furrow wheel, the rear furrow wheel axle should be moved up until there is 1/2-inch space beneath heel of the landside on the rear bottom. On plows having rolling landside in place of rear wheel, no adjustment is necessary.

The depth or master lever on a tractor plow is used only for setting the depth. After the proper adjustment for depth is made, the plow is leveled, by adjusting the leveling lever, to insure a uniform, smooth job of plowing at the depth set.

The power lift built into the land wheel is simple and positive. The operator simply pulls the trip rope and the bottoms are lifted high and clear for turning or transporting. When the turn is completed, the bottoms are lowered by pulling the rope in the same fashion. The power lift shown in Fig. 64, is of a new type designed for especially long life. Greased and

Figure 62—The two-furrow two-way plow at work.

sealed at the factory, it requires no periodic change of lubricant and no adjustment.

The lifting spring should have proper tension. If the spring has too much tension, it will cause the land wheel to slide when plow enters the ground. If not tight enough, the land wheel may slide a little when plow is being lifted. Adjust by loosening or tightening.

When plows are equipped for remote control through a hydraulic cylinder actuated by the tractor power lift (Fig. 63), all operating field adjustments are made by the operator from the tractor seat. The power lift of the tractor, operating through the remote cylinder attached to the plow, raises and lowers the bottoms and varies the depth as required in field operation. When depth of plowing is to be changed greatly, the plow must be leveled by means of leveling lever or crank on the plow.

Figure 63—A two-bottom plow with hydraulic control.

The hitch for tractor plows should be one of two types—the pin-break type, equipped with medium strength pin, or the cushion-spring-release type. In the first type, the wood pin breaks when a field obstruction is met; with the cushion-spring-release type, the load is carried on heavy coil springs which are compressed when the load becomes too great, thereby permitting the hitch to release the plow.

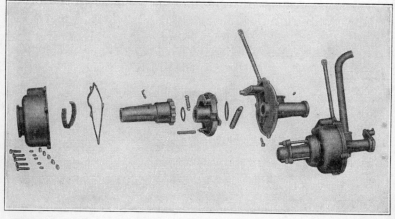

Figure 64—The enclosed power lift is shown completely assembled and "exploded" to show component parts. The entire lift is sealed to exclude dirt and to retain oil. Principal parts shown are: cover; felt strip; gasket; box; lifting clutch; and axle journal assembly.

A modern example of the cushion-spring-release or safety hitch is shown in Fig. 65. Clevis ring is latched to the revolving hook which revolves on the long U-bolt which carries the two compression springs. Under normal field conditions, the load is cushioned by the springs, since the pull is applied to the springs through the U-bolt. As the strain becomes too great or when a field obstruction is encountered, the springs are compressed, permitting the revolving hook to make a half-turn, releasing the plow. As the load is released, the revolving hook snaps back to position ready for rehitching. Rehitching is accomplished simply by raising the hitch and backing the tractor into position and dropping the hitch latch into the clevis ring.

The safety hitch, an important protection for both the plow and the tractor, should be kept at proper tension if it is to act as a safety device. Never draw up the springs to the point where too much tension is created, for in doing so the purpose of the hitch is defeated. Keep the revolving hook (or latch on the latch-type hitch) lubricated so that it can serve efficiently as a safeguard to your equipment.

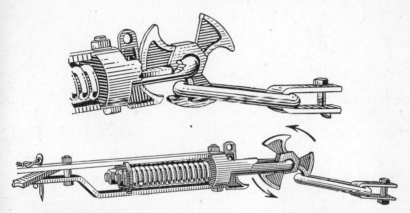

Figure 65—Cushion-spring-release hitch. Cutaway view above shows revolving hook in pulling position. Lower illustration shows springs compressed under load, permitting hook to revolve, releasing the plow.

Care of Tractor Plows. It is a good plan to go over the plow before storing, and to put it in condition for the next season's work. Sharpen shares or get new ones if the old ones are too badly worn; tighten bolts, replacing where needed; readjust or replace any parts that show excessive wear. Reconditioning plows during slack seasons saves time in the busy plowing season.

While the plow requires but little servicing in the field, what servicing is required is highly important. Thorough lubrication at correct intervals, a frequent check of coulter and jointer adjustment, and inspection of shares and sharpening when necessary, will do much to insure fine field performance from your plow.

Hitching Tractor Plows. The most important factor in tractor plow operation is correct hitching. Draft, quality of work, and ease of operation depend, to a great extent, upon the hitch.

In hitching the tractor plow as in the hitching of any wheel plow, keep in mind the fact that when the plow is at work, the

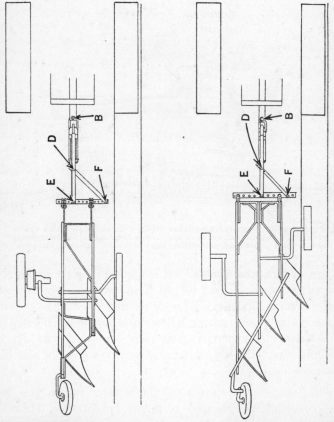

Figure 66—Correct horizontal hitch for two-bottom tractor plows.

Figure 67—Illustrating how to adjust horizontal hitch for three-bottom tractor plows.

wheels serve to carry the weight of the plow and the earth being turned, and to act as gauge wheels to keep the plow bottoms level at uniform depth. The principals of center of load in relation to center of power must be observed. Figs. 66, 67, and 68 illustrate the correct horizontal and vertical hitches for two- and three-bottom tractor plows.

Fig. 66 illustrates the correct horizontal hitch for two-bottom tractor plows. Attach drawbars at "E" and "F", as shown. Adjust drawbar at "D", to make front bottom cut right size furrow slice.

Fig. 67 shows proper horizontal hitch adjustment for three-bottom tractor plows. With drawbars attached as shown at "E" and "F", width of cut of front bottom is regulated by adjustment at point "D".

Fig. 68 shows the correct vertical hitch of tractor plows. The line from center of draft, point "C", should pass through hitch at "A", to point of attachment to tractor. If this line is broken by raising hitch at point "A", the resulting down-pull on front of plow tends to raise rear of plow out of the ground. Likewise, too low a hitch at "A" will raise front end of plow.

Careful adjustment of the hitch insures an even-running plow, a good job of plowing.

How to Plow a Field. Where fields are plowed in "lands", a definite plan is necessary to good plowing and time-saving with a tractor plow. The plan of opening and plowing in

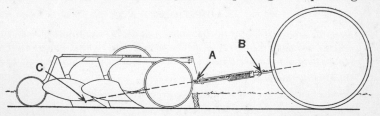

Figure 68—Correct vertical hitch for tractor plows, "A", is on straight line from center of draft, "C", to point of hitch to tractor drawbar at "B".

lands, as shown in Fig. 69, has been found very practical. It reduces to a minimum the amount of time spent in turning and moving with the bottoms out of the ground. Details of this plan are given with the illustration.

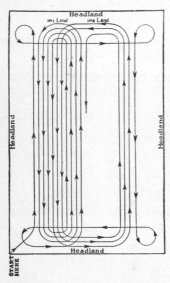

Figure 69—Plan for laying out and plowing a field with a tractor and plow: First—Stake out headland, about twice the length of the outfit, clear around the field. This gives all room necessary for turning at ends. Second—Plow a furrow clear around the field, as staked out. These furrows may be thrown in or out. However, it is recommended to throw in, as this leaves the headland in better shape to finish. Then, too, the head furrows mark the point to raise and lower the plow. To begin the furrow, drop the plow when the first bottom reaches the dead furrow. This leaves square headlands. Third—Open land as shown in diagram; arrows show direction of travel. After land No. 1 has become too narrow to permit the sweeping turn, swing over and open up land No. 2, plowing alternate furrows in both lands until land No. 1 is finished. Then plow land No. 2 until it is too narrow for turning; open the third land and so on. Fourth—After all lands are plowed, start in at one corner and plow around until the entire headland is plowed and field finished.

On contoured land, plowing should be done as near as possible to parallel the contour lines. The actual operation will vary so widely from field to field that it is impossible to give instructions to meet all conditions in a book of this type.

Questions

1. *Describe several types of tractor plows and tell the conditions to which they are adapted. What type is most generally used in your community?*

2. *How would you adjust the rear wheel of a tractor plow for best work?*

3. *What is the purpose of the leveling lever?*

4. *What is the purpose of a cushion-spring-release hitch?*

5. *How would you obtain the correct vertical hitch on a tractor plow? The correct horizontal hitch?*

6. *How would you open a field for plowing with a tractor?*

Disk Plows

Types and Uses. Disk plows are used in territories where soil conditions are such that moldboard plows will not operate to best advantage. They work well in soil so dry and hard that moldboard plows cannot penetrate, and in sticky soils, such as waxy muck, gumbo, and hardpan, where moldboard plows will not scour well. They are also used to advantage in very loose ground and in stony and rooty land.

The disk plow illustrated in Fig. 70 is a popular size for use with the medium sized farm tractor. In addition to this size, there are lighter and heavier plows of similar design, and integral or tractor-carried types (Fig. 72) built for use with the modern general purpose type tractor. For use with larger, heavier, more powerful tractors there are several types of heavy-duty and extra heavy-duty plows (Fig. 73) designed to meet the toughest plowing jobs encountered.

Operation and Adjustment. Since all disk plows operate on practically the same principles, the plow shown in Fig. 70, will serve as a basis for this discussion.

Disks must operate at the same level to do an even job of plowing. The rear wheel may be raised or lowered by the

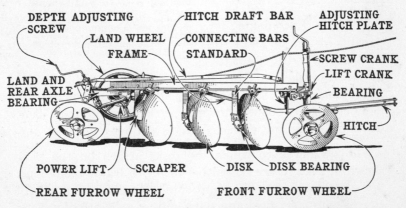

Figure 70—Tractor-drawn disk plow with important parts named.

adjustment of a simple eccentric to fix its proper relation to the level at which the disks run.

The front furrow wheel will run straight when the steering bar is adjusted properly so that front disk cuts full width. When opening lands, it is sometimes necessary to raise the furrow wheel higher than ordinarily required, by turning the screw crank depth adjustment. After opening lands restore adjustments so that all disks cut uniform depth.

Scrapers must be set so they barely touch near the center of the disk, with the wing 1/4-inch from the surface. If set too close, excessive friction is created; if too far they will not do a good job of cleaning.

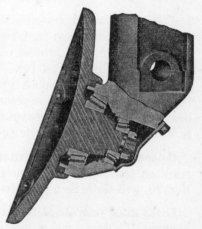

Adjusting Load to Power. Practically all disk plows are convertible in number of disks used and the cut per disk, making it possible for the operator to fit the total width of cut to

Figure 71—Showing cross-sectional view of roller bearing disk bearing with disk removed. Tapered roller bearings installed at spindle and shoulder carry the pressure of plowing with a minimum of draft. Expanding felt collar and overlapping flange on the disk spindle make this bearing dirtproof.

the power available and to soil conditions. In some of the larger heavy-duty plows, one disk may be removed and the remaining disks re-spaced, in which setting the plow cuts same width as before, but each disk takes a wider cut.

The standards to which the disks attach on the plow shown in Fig. 70 are bolted between two frame bars. They are adjustable vertically to provide three different angles of the disks to meet field and soil conditions. Width of cut per disk is increased or decreased by changing the angle of the frame. This is done by shifting the rear frame.

Care Important. The disks of a disk plow are important factors in its operation. If they are kept sharp, polished, and properly adjusted, they cut and turn the furrow slices with the least possible draft. If neglected, they soon become the source of penetration troubles and poor work—the disk surfaces should be oiled when not in use. The wheel boxings should be kept well greased with a good grade of hard oil.

The roller bearing disk bearing, cross-section of which is shown in Fig. 71, does not require adjusting; it is lubricated by means of a pressure lubrication fitting.

Hitch Adjustments. The same relation between power and load that governs the hitching of moldboard plows applies to disk plows. The vertical hitch must be such that the pull of tractor or horses holds the plow steadily to the depth set without raising or lowering the front end. A trial hitch

Figure 72—The integral disk plow makes up a compact, easily-handled plowing unit with the general purpose tractor.

and observation of results will indicate the proper hole in which to hitch.

The horizontal hitch should be as near as possible in direct line with the center of draft which is approximately the center of the total width of cut on any type of disk plow. Adjustment right or left may be necessary, in which case the furrow wheel may require adjustment so that the front disk cuts proper width.

Figure 73—Preparing a seedbed, in tough conditions, with a heavy-duty disk plow capable of working as deep as twenty inches.

Questions

1. *Under what conditions are disk plows used?*
2. *Name and describe two types of disk plows.*
3. *What is necessary to do an even job of plowing?*
4. *How would you increase or decrease the width of cut per disk?*
5. *What are the most important points in caring for a disk plow?*
6. *How would you obtain the proper hitch adjustment?*

Disk Tillers

The disk tiller Figs. 74, 75, 76, and 77 is similar in operation to the disk plow. Introduced originally as big-capacity, time-saving tillage equipment for the winter wheat growers, it is gaining great popularity with general farmers in practically all parts of the country. Once over after harvest puts the land in condition for planting in some sections; in other sections, it is common practice to till the ground once after harvesting and again just before planting.

The disk tiller has proved so successful in many general farming sections that its use is no longer restricted to one territory—a fact which has resulted in the development of tillers in various sizes and in modified types to take care of a wide range of uses in weeding, seedbed preparation, working fallow ground, building and maintaining terraces, etc. Seeding attachments are now available for many tillers, thereby broadening the usefulness of this versatile equipment.

The kind of work a disk tiller will do depends much upon the condition of its disks and bearings. Disks must be sharp

Figure 74—Disk tiller equipped with hydraulic cylinder for control from tractor seat.

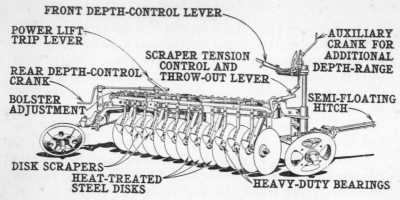

FRONT DEPTH-CONTROL LEVER

POWER LIFT
TRIP LEVER

AUXILIARY
CRANK FOR
ADDITIONAL
DEPTH-RANGE

SCRAPER TENSION
CONTROL AND
THROW-OUT LEVER

REAR DEPTH-CONTROL
CRANK

BOLSTER
ADJUSTMENT

SEMI-FLOATING
HITCH

DISK SCRAPERS

HEAT-TREATED
STEEL DISKS

HEAVY-DUTY BEARINGS

Figure 75—Disk tiller, used in preparing wheatland.

to cut the stubble and trash, and their bearings well oiled to withstand the heavy work to which they are subjected.

Adjustment and operation of the tiller are comparatively simple. The fundamental principles which govern proper hitching apply to the disk tiller.

In the field, a long lever at the front, supplemented by an auxiliary crank for additional range, controls depth of the front furrow wheel. This control device provides plenty of adjustment for opening up land. An easily-operated screw crank at the rear acts upon both the land and rear wheels. Once leveled to the proper depth, no further adjustment is necessary as the power lift raises the disks or drops them to work when turning at the headlands. The correct hitch is on a straight line between center of draft and point of attachment to tractor. A trial will usually show where the hitch should be.

The adaptability of hydraulic control through the remote cylinder is especially important to the operation of a disk tiller, see Fig. 74. With this control, the operator may vary the depth instantly to meet field conditions as the outfit moves over the field. The remote cylinder, of course, is used to raise and lower the tiller in addition to its function in making field adjustments.

Figure 76—Disk tiller at work. Note how stubble is mixed with the surface soil, forming a mulch.

A bolster adjustment on the rear of the tiller, shown on the preceding pages, provides adjustment for changing the angle at which the disks work. By means of this adjustment, any working angle required to meet conditions ranging from soft, loose soil, to hard, dry ground can be obtained. The rear

Figure 77—A small disk tiller working on terrace maintenance.

frame is definitely marked with settings for three soil conditions: "soft or stony ground", "medium ground", and "hard ground".

The rear gang of three disks on the tiller, shown in Fig. 75, may be removed to reduce the load where field conditions are unusually difficult. This reduces the width of cut, lessening the power required. Many of the smaller tillers are reducible in size in the same manner although the smallest sizes, built for the small tractors, are reducible in cut by varying the angle of the disk gang only.

Questions

1. Describe the disk tiller, its advantages and uses.
2. How is depth controlled on the tiller shown?
3. What is the purpose of the bolster adjustment?
4. Why is hydraulic control especially valuable in the operation of the disk tiller?

Chapter III.

DISK HARROWS

The function of the disk harrow is to pulverize and pack the soil, leaving a surface mulch and a compact subsurface. It is used to good advantage before plowing to break the surface and mix the trash with the topsoil and, after plowing, to pulverize lumps and close air spaces in the turned furrows. Although it is not to be found on every farm, there are few general farmers who would not profit by its use. Fig. 78 illustrates the value of a disk harrow when used before and after plowing.

Types of Disk Harrows. Disk harrows are made in single-action and double-action types. Some types of single-action harrows can be converted into double-action harrows by adding a rear section. In addition to these standard types, special harrows are built for use in orchards and groves. These harrows are usually offset to work up close to trees while the tractor operates away from the row where it will not interfere with low-hanging branches. Heavy-duty types are available for use in conditions which require harrows of greater strength for deeper penetration.

Requirements for Good Work. To do a good job, the

Sun-Baked Stubble Land

Plowed, but Not Disked

Disked After Plowed, but Not Before. Notice Air Spaces

Disked and then Plowed. Good Contact with Subsoil

Disked Before and After Plowed. The Ideal Seedbed

Figure 78—Drawings illustrating the value of disking both before and after plowing.

disk harrow, first of all, must penetrate well and evenly over its entire width. In the case of two-section machines, both sections must meet these requirements, the disks of the rear section cutting the ridges left by the front disks instead of trailing in their furrows.

Flexibility has much to do with even penetration and good work. When the gangs of each section work independently, one gang may pass over stones or stumps and conform to irregularities in the surface of the field without hindering the work of the other gangs.

Proper penetration is most important in the proper functioning of a disk harrow. Securing good penetration depends upon several factors.

The design of the harrow is of utmost importance, for good design presupposes proper distribution of weight with ample strength to meet field conditions. Present-day harrows, reflecting the trend to improved manufacturing methods are, in many cases, lighter in weight than were the earlier harrows; however, through improved design they have greater

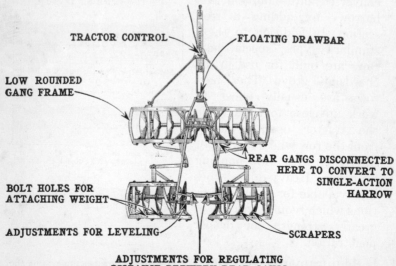

Figure 79—A double-action tractor-controlled disk harrow.

strength and will penetrate and hold to their work effectively. Weight crates or platforms are provided on most modern harrows so that additional weight may be used where difficult conditions require it.

Operation and Adjustments. Penetration of a disk harrow is obtained by angling the disks, the angle necessary for good work depending upon the condition (or texture) of the soil and the amount of trash to be cut. On most disk harrows, provision is made for angling the disks for maximum penetration which is obtained at an angle of approximately 20 degrees.

Angling the gangs of both the single- and double-action harrows (Figs. 79, 80, and 82) is accomplished by means of trip ropes within reach of the tractor operator. Gangs of both the single-action and the double-action harrow can be straightened on the forward pull if in danger of stalling the tractor.

Front and rear gangs of the double-action harrow can be angled to the proper degree or straightened independently of each other.

Hydraulic control, as applied to the disk harrow, shown in Fig. 81, enables the operator to angle or straighten the gangs without stopping the forward travel of the tractor.

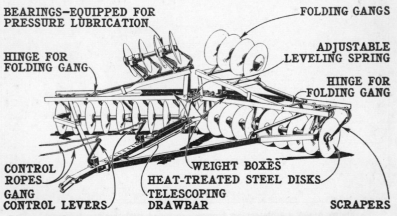

BEARINGS—EQUIPPED FOR PRESSURE LUBRICATION

FOLDING GANGS

HINGE FOR FOLDING GANG

ADJUSTABLE LEVELING SPRING

HINGE FOR FOLDING GANG

CONTROL ROPES

GANG CONTROL LEVERS

WEIGHT BOXES

HEAT-TREATED STEEL DISKS

TELESCOPING DRAWBAR

SCRAPERS

Figure 80—Single-action tractor-controlled harrow with end gangs folded over.

The end gangs of the single-action harrow, shown in Fig. 80, can be folded over when going through gateways, or to provide additional weight for better penetration in difficult conditions. In this way, a 15-foot harrow can be narrowed to 10-1/2 feet, and a 21-foot harrow to 14 feet. The single-action harrow may be used for double-disking by lapping half the width of the machine each time across the field.

The scrapers are adjustable to suit soil conditions. Scrapers on both sections of the double-action tractor harrows shown can be oscillated by means of ropes, without leaving the tractor seat. Pressure on foot levers on the horse-drawn models oscillates scrapers.

Provision is made for locking scrapers at the edges of disks, or for locking them away from disks when not needed.

Good Care Lengthens Life. The efficiency and length of service of a disk harrow depend upon the care given it.

First in importance is thorough greasing of the bearings. Many of the modern disk harrows, especially the tractor types, are equipped with fittings for pressure lubrication, making it an easy matter to keep the bearings well oiled.

Figure 81—A double-action harrow equipped with hydraulic control.

Where hard oilers are used, cups should be kept full of a good grade of hard oil and should be turned down at regular intervals. The bearing bushings are provided with fittings for grease-gun lubrication to make thorough lubrication an easy servicing job.

A good cutting edge on all disks is desirable, especially in hard ground and trashy conditions. Most disk blades are now made of tough steel, then heat-treated to hold a long-wearing edge.

During slack seasons, go over the entire disk harrow, tightening bolts, replacing worn parts, and getting the implement ready for the next season's work. Keep disks well greased with a good hard oil when harrow is not in use.

Questions

1. *What is the function of the disk harrow?*
2. *Why should it be used both before and after plowing?*
3. *What is the first requirement of a disk harrow?*
4. *What is meant by "flexibility" and why is it desirable?*
5. *How is a disk harrow made to penetrate?*
6. *How are the scrapers oscillated?*
7. *Why is it necessary to keep the disks sharp?*

Figure 82—A tractor-controlled single-action disk harrow doing good work.

Chapter IV.

HARROWS, PULVERIZERS, AND FIELD CULTIVATORS

Methods of finishing the seedbed vary according to soil conditions and established practices in different sections of the country. While the spike-tooth harrow is used in practically every section, the spring-tooth harrow, pulverizer, and field or tool-bar cultivator are not in such general use. For that reason, the discussion of those implements will be brief.

Spike-Tooth Harrows. Fig. 83 shows a popular style of spike-tooth harrow. The operation and adjustment of a harrow of this type are comparatively simple, there being no field adjustment other than setting the slant of the teeth with the levers provided. This adjustment is governed entirely by field conditions.

Each tooth of this harrow is held between two notched, semi-oval frame bars by a heavy bolt which creates a tension, thereby locking the tooth to position and preventing the nut from coming loose. When one side of the tooth becomes worn, the nut may be loosened and the tooth turned to present a new cutting edge. Teeth may also be removed for sharpening.

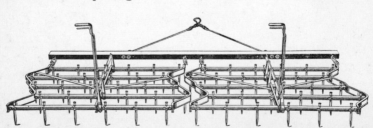

Figure 83—Spike-tooth harrow with detail above showing how tooth is locked between bars.

**Spring-Tooth Har-
rows.** The fact that
spring-tooth harrows
will penetrate to a
greater depth than
spike-tooth harrows
makes them better

Figure 84—A three-section, tractor-controlled, spring-tooth harrow.

adapted to the requirements of certain sections. They are
used also with great efficiency in the eradication of obnoxious
weeds and grasses.

Fig. 84 illustrates a tractor spring-tooth harrow that is
controlled from the tractor seat. Trip ropes are provided
for dropping the teeth to work and raising them out of the
ground, depth being determined by previous setting. In
addition to this depth adjustment, the individual teeth may
be adjusted in the clamps for finer depth adjustment or to
vary the penetration.

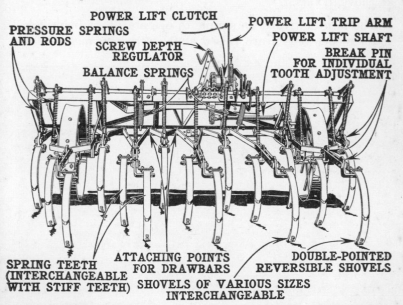

Figure 85—Field and orchard cultivator with tractor hitch and screw-type depth
regulator.

Several styles of teeth may be obtained for different purposes such as cultivating alfalfa and digging out quack-grass roots, in addition to the type used as a seedbed finisher.

Field and Orchard Cultivators. Because of its great diversity of uses, the field cultivator is used extensively in both the United States and Canada. The type shown in Fig. 85, low-down, with wheels set inside the frame, is ideal for working close to trees, fences, and ditches, in both field and orchard.

It is used for preparing fall-plowed land for spring seeding, and for tillage work in regions where summer-fallowing is practiced. It does good work as a weed destroyer, eradicating quack-grass, thistle, wild morning-glory, and other weeds; it is also an efficient alfalfa cultivator.

The field cultivator, shown in Fig. 85, may be used with either stiff- or spring-teeth and with different kinds and sizes of shovel points.

The field cultivator is simple to operate, there being few adjustments. Teeth are raised and lowered by means of a

Figure 86—The tool-bar cultivator with sub-surface sweeps, destroying surface growth.

power lift operated by a trip rope from tractor seat or by hydraulic power from the tractor power lift through a remote cylinder. Crank-type depth regulator gives tractor operator constant depth control.

Frequent sharpening of the shovels, and keeping them coated with a good hard oil when not in use, will aid in making the cultivator pull light and do good work.

Similar to the field cultivator in the variety of work it does and equipment available for it, the sub-surface cultivator (Fig. 86) is designed for the heavier tillage work. Working equipment, shovels, sweeps, spring teeth, etc., is quickly interchangeable on the long tool bar. Spacing of equipment is varied by shifting the tool clamps. Like the field cultivator discussed above, the tool-bar cultivator is raised and lowered by a power lift built into the wheel, or by hydraulic power which permits the operator to raise, lower, and make field depth changes from the tractor seat. The tool-bar cultivator requires little field servicing other than periodic lubrication and check for loose parts.

Soil Pulverizer. Ideal for finishing the seedbed and valuable for use in growing crops, the soil pulverizer, or packer, is more widely used each year. It is simple and easy to operate. There are no adjustments and few parts that ever need replacing, with exception, possibly, of the oil-soaked wood boxings which are easily removed and replaced at small cost.

Questions

1. *What implements are used for finishing seedbeds in your community?*
2. *What adjustment can be made on the teeth of the spike-tooth harrow shown?*
3. *To what conditions are spring-tooth harrows especially adapted?*
4. *Describe a field cultivator and its uses.*
5. *For what purposes is the tool-bar cultivator used? How does it differ from the field and orchard cultivator?*
6. *Why is the soil pulverizer a valuable implement for finishing the seedbed?*

Part Three
PLANTING

The necessity of planting all crops at the proper depth and distributing uniformly the right amount of seed to suit soil conditions is quite apparent to all who have had experience in growing products of the soil.

If seed is planted too deep or too shallow, too thick or too thin, if the row planter skips hills or the grain drill leaves strips unplanted, the yield is bound to be reduced accordingly. If planted accurately, with the per-acre quantity carefully measured to suit the richness of the soil, maximum yields will result, provided of course, that other conditions and practices are correct.

The farmer who understands and gives careful thought to the adjustment and operation of his planting equipment will profit greatly. The operation of planting equipment should be studied carefully by the students of agriculture and farm mechanics.

Chapter V.
GRAIN DRILLS

Grain drills have been improved greatly during the past few years. Perhaps the most notable improvement is the steel box. Not only does the steel construction give greater strength and durability, but it also makes possible an enormous increase in capacity, in some cases, as much as 72 percent more than that of the wood box.

Like plows, grain drills are built in many different styles with a variety of equipment to meet conditions in every section of the country. In some sections, the single-disk furrow opener will work better than the double-disk, while other conditions may demand a hoe-type opener. The big farm regions require big tractor-drawn drills while the small farmers of the East or South need only the smaller sizes. Many farmers in the larger wheat-growing sections prefer the double-run feed type of drill. In semi-arid regions, where every available bit of moisture must be conserved, the semi-deep furrow drill with its large disks solves the problem by placing the seed considerably deeper than the ordinary drill, thereby assuring contact with the moist soil found at greater depth. In territories where soil blowing is a serious problem, the deep furrow drill, with moldboards which throw the soil one way (Fig. 91) serves the purpose of deep planting and, at the same time, leaves the surface soil ridged to prevent or reduce soil drifting and seed blowing. But whatever the preference may be, or conditions demand, it is usually found that manufacturers build a drill that meets the requirements satisfactorily.

Types of Drills. There are three principal types of end-wheel grain drills—the fluted-feed, the double-run feed, and the combination grain and fertilizer drill. Of these, the fluted feed (Fig. 87) is in most general use, although in some sections the other styles are used almost exclusively. The double-run feed drills are favored in many territories,

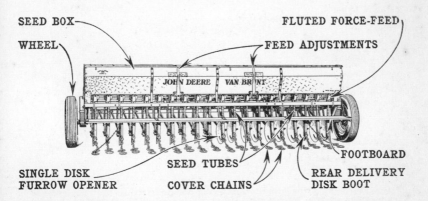

Figure 87—Rear view of grain drill equipped with single-disk openers.

while more and more farmers in all areas are coming to consider the combination fertilizer and grain drill as the most practical for their conditions. Then, there is the low-down press drill having press wheels that firm the soil over the seed to prevent it from blowing. The plow press drill, similar in construction, is attached behind the plow. A pulverizer may be used between the plow and the drill, making a three-way hook-up for plowing, pulverizing, and seeding, all in one operation.

Fluted Feed. The fluted force-feed consists mainly of a feed roll, feed cut-off, feed cup, and an adjustable gate. The feed roll turns with the shaft, forcing the grain out over

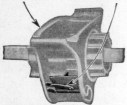

One-Piece Feed Cup   Latch in Upper Left Notch

Position 1—All gates up with latches in top notch at left side to sow all grains, small seeds, kafir corn, and beets.

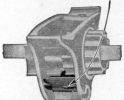

Latch in Right-Hand Notch

Position 2—Fasten all latches at right side to sow peas, common beans, soybeans, corn, and extra large quantities of trashy oats.

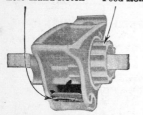

Latch in Lower Left-Hand Notch   Feed Roll

Position 3—Fasten all latches in lower notch on left side to sow soybeans marrow fat, or kidney beans.

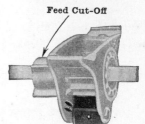

Feed Cut-Off

Position 4—Drop gates to clean feeds.

Figure 88—Detail of the fluted-feed showing different settings that can be made for planting seeds of various sizes. Quantity is controlled by shifting the feed roll and feed cut-off to permit more or less of the feed roll to turn within the feed cup. This is done with the feed shaft shifter.

the feed gate which is adjustable for different sizes of seeds. The feed cut-off and the feed roll shift with the feed shaft, and their position determines the quantity of seed sown. The one-piece seed cups aid in maintaining accuracy because they do not become loose and get out of line. See Fig. 88 for detailed explanation.

Setting Fluted-Feed Drills for Quantity. The first adjustment in using any drill is to set it to sow the desired quantity per acre. This is done on fluted-feed drills by adjusting the feed shaft and the gates on the feeds to suit the size of seed and the quantity to be sown.

The setting of the adjustable-gate force feeds according to size of seed is described under the illustrations in Fig. 88. Before putting grain in the box, all gates should be let down as in No. 4, and all grain and accumulations cleaned out. To insure uniform planting, the latches on all feeds must be kept in same position while seeding.

The feed adjustment, or feed shaft shifter, moves the feed rolls and feed cut-offs to permit more or less grain to be forced out by the feed rolls. There are two of these shifters on drills having more than eight disks, one for each half of the drill. Both must be kept in the same position on the seed index plate, which is provided with a row of notches to hold shifters in position. These notches are numbered by the figures which are immediately above them. Figures above at left of notches indicate the amount of flax and alfalfa—in pounds—to be seeded per acre. Figures below notches indicate amount of oats, barley, wheat, and peas—in pounds—to be seeded per acre.

Double-Run Feed Drills. The double-run feed drill gets its name from its type of feed, illustration of which is shown in Fig. 89. The feed and the mechanism which drives it constitute the principal differences between this type of drill and the fluted-feed drill shown in Fig. 87.

Fig. 89 shows two views of the double-run feed. It consists mainly of a feed wheel and a feed gate. The

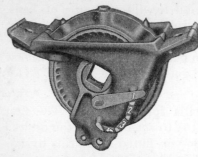

Lock lever on small side of feed, used for regulating inside quantity feed gate, and the positions at which it may be set. Numerals indicate the positions.

Showing adjustable-gate inside the feed cup for regulating size of the feed opening to handle different quantities of seed.

Figure 89—Detail view of double-run feed, showing large and small sides.

wheel is smaller on one side for use in planting small seeds. The large side is used for planting oats, barley, treated wheat, peas, beans, and other large seeds.

The adjustable gates, which are inside the feed cups, regulate the size of the feed openings, there being eight different positions at which they can be set—four on each side. These adjustments provide eight different quantity adjustments for each one of the five multiple gears, making a total of 40 different quantities in which seed may be planted without changing gears. By reversing the intermediate gear, 40 additional quantity adjustments are provided—80 in all.

Fertilizer-Grain Drills. This type of drill completes four operations at once. It pulverizes the soil, plants seed, distributes fertilizer, and covers both. Farmers who find it necessary to sow fertilizer on their fields are able to make a big saving in time and money by using a fertilizer drill, sowing the fertilizer and seed in one operation.

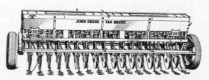

Figure 90—The fertilizer-grain drill is gaining in use where fertilizer proves valuable in securing better yields.

Fertilizer drills have two distributing units—one for seed and one for fertilizer—although both seed and fertilizer are released through the same tube. The planting unit, which consists of the regular fluted-feed drill mechanism, illustrated in Fig. 88, is built into the front half of the seed box. The fertilizer feed distributes any amount of fertilizer from 24 to 1680 pounds per acre. Star feeder wheels rotate in the fertilizer box and cause an even flow of material into the seed tubes.

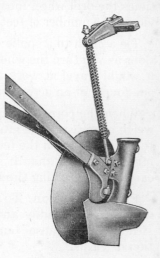

Because of the increasing use of highly-concentrated fertilizer, a number of drill manufacturers are now offering a special fertilizer attachment for all types of drills which keeps the fertilizer from coming in contact with the seed. The fertilizer is released through separate tubes and deposited in the rows, but there is always a layer of

Figure 91—F u r r o w opener with mold-board as used on deep furrow drill.

soil between the fertilizer and the seed. The depth is controlled by a simple adjustment on the fertilizer boot.

Operation and adjustment of fertilizer-grain drills, with exception of the fertilizer unit, is the same as given for fluted-feed drills in a preceding paragraph.

Calibrating Grain Drills. The operator should be sure to have his drill set properly before starting to sow. If there is doubt in his mind as to the accuracy of his machine, he may make the calibration test which follows:

To check the accuracy of a grain drill, jack it up in working position, fill the box with grain, place a canvas in position to catch the grain, and set the gates and feed shifters properly. Find the total width of strip planted each time across the field. Divide 43,560—the number of square feet in an acre—by the width of strip planted and you have the length of a strip necessary to make one acre. Then find the number of times the drill wheel must turn in going this distance by dividing the number of feet by the circumference of the wheel.

Tie a cloth to a spoke of the wheel and count the revolutions as you turn the wheel, turning at about the same speed it would travel at work. You need not sow a whole acre—one-fourth of an acre is sufficient for the test.

When the correct number of revolutions has been made, weigh or measure the grain on the canvas and check it with the adjustment on the feed-shifter scale. If the drill is planting more or less than it should, the difference can be taken care of by adjusting the feed shifters.

Field Operation. To do a good job of sowing, the drill must be run steadily and evenly. Swinging of poles or unsteady driving causes bunching of seed and results in reduction of yields.

The depth of seeding over full width of the drill is controlled by the lifting levers and by a pressure spring on each

Figure 92—Seeding with the double-disk fertilizer drill.

furrow opener. When pressure is applied to the furrow openers, it should be uniform. Uniform pressure can be gained
only by having both lifting levers in the same notch and hav-

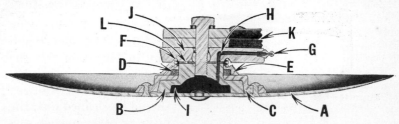

Figure 93—Cross-section of drill disk showing "A", disk blade; "B", disk bearing; "C", bearing case; "D", felt washer; "E", hard-iron dust cap; "F",
dust cap spring; "G", Alemite fitting; "H", oil passage; "I", oil
reservoir; "J", disk boot casting; "K", drawbar; "L", gasket.

ing the pressure on all springs the
same. The pressure on each furrow
opener is adjusted by raising or lowering the adjusting collar on the pressure
rod.

The tilting levers on rear of poles
provide easy adjustment for proper
relation between penetration and
depth of planting when using any
type of furrow opener.

Disk scrapers should be adjusted as
lightly as practical and disengaged entirely, when possible, to prevent wear.

The land measurer is provided to
measure the number of acres covered
by the drill. On some drills, the land
measurer is driven from the main

Figure 94—Cutaway view
of double-disk opener
showing how seed is pro-
tected between disks until
it reaches the open furrow.

axles; on others, from the feed shaft. To set it when starting a
new field, press top of measurer in to force the bottom gear
out of contact with worm gear on feed shaft or axle. Turn
bottom gear to right—about 1/8 of an acre—to disengage
fraction gear from acre gear. Move the indicator to largest

Figure 95—Hoe-type of furrow opener with spring-trip.

number on acre dial and turn bottom gear to left, with indicator on fraction dial in upward position.

Care of Drills. The drill should be cleaned and put in condition for the next season's seeding before it is stored. All seed should be cleaned out, the disks or other opener surfaces cleaned and oiled, and the machine put under shelter. Good treatment prolongs the life of the drill.

Most drills are equipped with fittings for pressure-gun lubrication. The disk bearings should be kept oiled thoroughly with oil or grease of proper viscosity as listed in the manufacturer's instruction book. Bear in mind that the disk bearings operate largely below the surface of the ground and, for that reason, it is highly important to keep the oil chamber well filled with oil of proper grade. See the cross-section of disk and bearing, Fig. 93. Double-disk openers are oiled from the top of the boot.

Types of Openers. Fig. 94 shows a cutaway view of a double-disk furrow opener, illustrating how seed is protected in seed tube and between disks until it reaches the bottom of the furrow.

Fig. 95 illustrates the hoe-type of opener which is especially adapted to seeding in rocky soils.

Fig. 96 shows a single-disk opener with pressure spring, scraper, and disk boot.

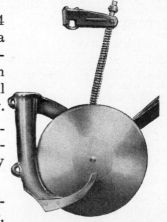

Figure 96—Single-Disk Opener.

The single-disk deep furrow opener is used with 12-, 14-, or 16-inch spacing to make wide, deep trenches and ridge the soil to catch the moisture and prevent the soil from blowing. It is used most widely in winter-wheat sections.

The deep furrow opener with moldboard and seed deflector is shown in Fig. 91.

All of these types of furrow openers are interchangeable.

Questions

1. What is the relation between planting and crop yields?
2. What is considered good planting of the crops grown in your community?
3. Describe the fluted-feed and tell how you would adjust it for quantity.
4. Describe the double-run type of feed and its adjustment.
5. What are the advantages of a fertilizer drill?
6. How and why would you calibrate a grain drill?
7. How is depth of sowing controlled?
8. What are the important points to remember in caring for grain drills when in operation and between seasons?
9. What type of furrow opener is used in your community and why?

Chapter VI.

ROW-CROP PLANTERS

Accurate planting has more to do with yields of row-crops than any other single mechanical factor. If more seed is planted than the soil will support, the individual plants will not produce to fullest possibility; if less seed is planted than the soil will support, planting time and land are wasted—the farmer is not getting full return from his investment in time and capital. The importance of proper seeding takes on added significance as the practice of fertilizing at planting time increases the initial investment and prospect of yield.

Corn Planters. Corn is grown in every state of the Nation. It is the principal crop throughout the corn belt and its importance in other areas of the country places corn planters first in our discussion.

While there is a definite trend to contour farming and, consequently, to drilled corn, the majority of corn in the corn belt is cross-checked. Here the mechanical accuracy

Figure 97—Planting at high speed on a corn belt farm.

of the planter in dropping the right number of seed for full yield must be combined with accurate spacing to insure the perfect cross-check for easiest cross-cultivation. If hills are crowded, barren stalks and small ears result. If hills are missed, or if less than the desired number of seed is dropped, time and land are wasted. If hills are "out-of-check", difficulty will be encountered at cultivating time.

The illustrations in Fig. 98 picture the results of accurate and inaccurate planting when three stalks per hill are ideal for soil conditions. In poor soils, two stalks per hill are sufficient, while in very rich loam soils four stalks will do well. The inaccurate spacing of drilled corn will result in the same losses as pictured in Fig. 98.

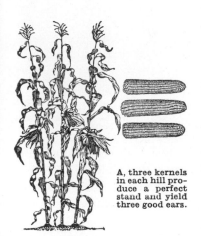

A, three kernels in each hill produce a perfect stand and yield three good ears.

Figure 98—Illustrations A, B, and C contrast the usual results of accurate and inaccurate planting when the soil will support three stalks of corn and produce three good ears in each hill.

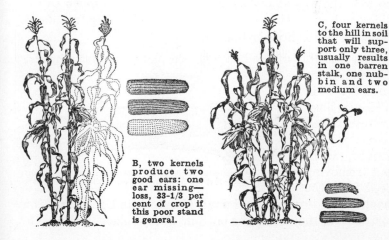

C, four kernels to the hill in soil that will support only three, usually results in one barren stalk, one nubbin and two medium ears.

B, two kernels produce two good ears: one ear missing— loss, 33-1/3 per cent of crop if this poor stand is general.

Drop and Seed Plates. The accuracy of a corn planter depends upon the accuracy of the drop and the selection of seed plates best suited to the size of seed to be planted—taking for granted, of course, that seed is of uniform size and that dirt has not clogged the seed passages.

There are two types of corn drops—the accumulative, and the full hill. The accumulative drop is generally conceded to be more accurate because it takes one seed to each cell in the seed plate and then counts out the number of seeds to a hill as desired. A full hill-drop planter takes all the seeds that make up the hill into

Figure 99—Top view of corn hopper bottom showing seed plate in position.

one cell. It is claimed, and probably rightly so, that it is easier to get one seed in a cell each time than it is to get more than one, the same number each time. The accumulative drop is described in the following paragraphs.

Fig. 100 shows a cross-section of a seed hopper bottom with seed plate in position. Note that the hopper bottom is sloping so that the weight of the seed will cause it to move to the sides and enter the openings in seed plate. Fig. 99 shows top view of the hopper bottom.

The assembly of the hopper, seed plate, and bottom false plate is shown in Fig. 101. This also illustrates how seed plates are removed, without removing seed from the

Figure 100—Seed plate and hopper bottom cut to show sloping hopper bottom, sloping hopper wall, and oblique seed plate.

hopper, by tipping the hopper forward and releasing the spring latch that holds the bottom plate in place. Extra-wide seed is accommodated by reversing the false bottom plate as indicated in the drawing.

Seed plates are now available for seed of any size from kafir to lima beans, including a full range of plates for handling the various hybrid strains of corn. Fig. 102 illustrates the importance of selecting the right seed plates by fitting the seed to be planted in the seed cells as shown. If cells are too large,

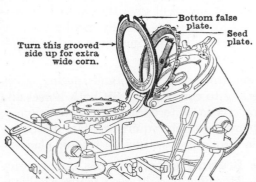

Turn this grooved side up for extra wide corn.

Bottom false plate.

Seed plate.

Figure 101—Assembly of the hopper, seed plate, and false plate showing how seed plates are removed by tipping hopper forward.

two kernels may pass into one cell, resulting in overcrowding the hill; if too small, less than the wanted number of kernels will be dropped.

Checking or Drilling. Practically all corn planters—horse- and tractor-drawn—can be used for both checking and drilling. The planters shown are easily adaptable for checking two, three, or four kernels per hill and for drilling seed in practically any spacing desired.

In drilling, seeds can be planted in any practical spacing desired. This wide range can be obtained by using plates having from two to twenty-four cells, setting the variable drop shifting lever on two,

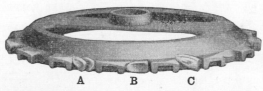

A   B   C

Figure 102—Illustrating how to select proper seed plates for an accumulative drop. Corn must fit the cells of the plate like the kernel marked "B". If kernels are too large as "C", or too small as "A", a plate having cells that will hold one kernel at a time should be selected.

three, or four, or using the drive chain on the large, medium, or small drive sprockets. A scale, showing how to set machine for any drilling distance, is provided with each planter. If this scale is not available, a few minutes spent in experimenting with various settings will give the desired adjustment. The plates used for checking usually can be used for drilling, the operator using the shifting lever and sprocket adjustments to get desired spacing.

The information on drop, seed plates, and spacing, given above, applies generally to corn planters of both horse- and tractor-drawn types. Basic differences in construction in these two types of planters which require separate discussion will be considered in a following section on tractor planters.

Checking Horse-Drawn Planters. To test the accuracy of the drop and to determine if right seed plates are being used, jack up the planter, fill hoppers with seed, and turn the wheels. Trip check forks by hand and catch the seed, keeping accurate check on each dropping. Planter should not be turned faster than 35 revolutions per minute.

To test for good cross-check, carefully dig up a row of at least eight hills crosswise to the direction of travel, and set

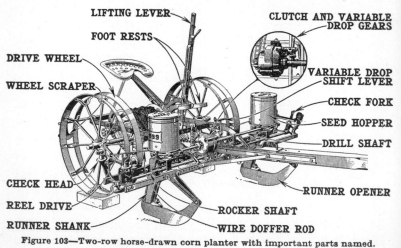

Figure 103—Two-row horse-drawn corn planter with important parts named.

a stake in center of each hill. (Due to the travel of wire, the hill of corn should be found about an inch behind the button.) An adjustment is provided on the planter which permits tilting front of planter to place hills closer to or farther from button. Tilting front by lowering runner tips places hills farther back, while raising runner tips places hills forward.

To adjust width of planter, remove bolts that hold shanks to frame, remove bolt holding drive pinion on drive shaft, and adjust the shanks in or out to width of row desired. Be careful not to slip pinion off the shaft as the timing will be disturbed. Adjust wheels in line with the runners.

Field Operation. The object of check-rowing corn is to make cross cultivation possible. Cultivating crosswise of the rows is a difficult task if checking is not straight, and the straightness of crossrows depends more than anything else upon the handling of the check-wire.

The check-wire should be stretched reasonably tight when laid out and should be kept at that tension. The reel friction can be adjusted to hold wire to the desired tautness when unwinding, but uniform checking depends upon the judgment of the operator in pulling the wire to the same tension each time he moves the stakes.

Crooked crossrows may also be caused by running front of the planter at an improper level, in which case every pair of rows will be out of check. This may be adjusted as explained in a preceding paragraph.

If only one side is out of check, it may be caused by incorrect adjustment of valves, frame of planter being bent, or by a weak rocker-shaft spring. A bent frame may also cause one row to be planted deeper than the other.

If the planter scatters seed between hills, the trouble may be due to kinks in the check-wire, an obstruction in the valves, or too little tension on the rocker-shaft spring.

Tractor Planters. With the advent of the row-crop tractor, farming operations generally stepped up in speed. This was true in practically all farming operations with exception of planting, which was restricted to horse speed because the type of valve in common use would not drop the seed quickly enough to prevent "strung-out" hills. Careful study of valve design proved definitely the reason why valves which were accurate to a high degree at slow speed became undependable at faster travel.

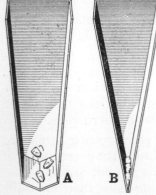

Figure 104—These two sketches show the principle involved in the horse-drawn planter valve and in the high-speed valve used in tractor planter. In "A" note that kernels falling to lower valve, bounce for a moment. In the high-speed valve, "B", seeds are wedged in the bottom of the valve to be released in a group. See further discussion on this page.

As the seed is released from the upper valve, it drops to the lower valve with sufficient momentum to cause it to rebound. See Fig. 104. At slow speed there is ample time between buttons to permit seed to settle in the valve before the valve opens. However, when this same valve is called upon to release 125 hills per minute in place of the 88 hills per minute for which it was de-

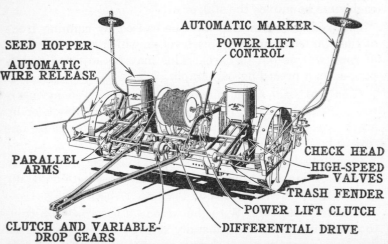

Figure 105—Two-row tractor planter designed for accurate planting at high speed.

signed, the hills were strung out and, in some cases, kernels were trapped in the valve. Now, consider what happens when kernels are dropped from upper to lower valve in the

Figure 106—Four-row tractor planter checking corn on a Mid-Western farm.

high speed planter. Dropping down the tapered tube the seeds are wedged as they fall—they have no opportunity for a "split-second" bounce that results in loss of accuracy.

The tractor-drawn planters, shown in Figs. 105 and 106, are similar in basic design to the horse-drawn planter described on preceding pages except, of course, that they are designed especially to plant accurately at the higher speeds of modern tractors.

The pressure wheel, set behind each runner, acts as an independent gauge wheel for each unit. As a result, each planting unit works independently of the others, thereby permitting each runner to ride over ridges or down into depressions without causing variation in planting depth of any of the other units. A power lift clutch on the planter (similar to that used on tractor plows) raises the planter runners and the disk marker at the same time.

The instructions that apply to the horse-drawn planter, as far as seed plates and adjustments are concerned, are so nearly applicable to the tractor planter that a separate discussion on the tractor planter is not necessary for our purposes.

Equipment and Attachments. Several combinations of disk and runner furrow openers can be obtained to suit different soil conditions. Gauge wheels or gauge shoes also can be obtained.

In many sections of the country, fertilizer is sown when the corn is planted. A fertilizer attachment for this purpose is provided by most manufacturers.

It is important that the fertilizer be kept from coming in direct contact with the seed, for if this occurs, the seed is "fired". The fertilizer attachment places a strip of fertilizer on each side of the hill after the seed has been partly covered with soil, so the fertilizer does not come in contact with the seed. Covering knives then throw soil over the fertilizer.

If it is desired to plant peas or beans along with the corn, the pea planting attachment may be added to the planter. Both the fertilizer and pea planting attachments can be used when planting corn, making it possible to plant two crops and sow fertilizer in one operation.

While planting accuracy depends almost entirely on the drop and the selection of seed plates, the tongue truck (on horse-drawn planters) is an important factor in obtaining a more accurate check and better all-around results, especially in hilly land. It eliminates neck weight and up-and-down movement of the planter, reduces sideslip on hillsides, assures more uniform planting depth and better covering of the seed, permits driving the planter straighter, and assures easier turning at row ends. Planters can be furnished with tongue truck, or the tongue truck may be purchased as a separate unit and attached by the owner.

Combination Cotton and Corn Planters. The cotton grower requires a planter that will plant cotton, corn, and other row-crops with equal accuracy. His multi-purpose planter must be quickly and easily convertible from one type of planter to another.

There are several types of combination cotton and corn planters, each designed to meet planting conditions common to a certain section.

Fig. 107 illustrates the type of mule- or horse-drawn planter most generally used where cotton is raised on ridges. This machine can be obtained with either runner or shovel opener. Fig. 108 shows a type of two-row planter available for both drilling and checking. One-row walking planters are also made for hill-dropping and drilling cotton and corn.

More recent equipment for the power farmer is the planting and fertilizing equipment which is used in conjunction with the tractor cultivator. Equipment of this type offers several important advantages. Mounted on the cultivator frame, it makes use of the cultivator parts as framework for the planting and fertilizing equipment. At cultivating time, the planting and fertilizing equipment is removed, shovels placed in position, and the unit becomes a tractor cultivator. At planting time, the cultivating parts are removed

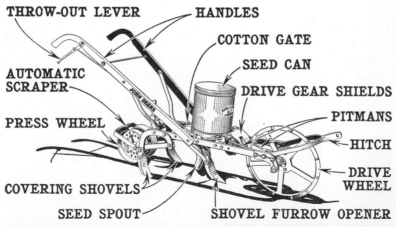

Figure 107—One-row combination cotton and corn planter with parts named.

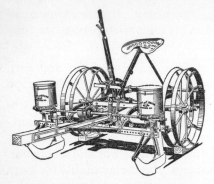

Figure 108—Two-row combined cotton and corn planter.

and planting and fertilizing equipment is replaced. While the unit of this type shown in Fig. 109 is equipped with sweep-type furrow openers and shovel coverers, different furrow openers and coverers are available for planting requirements in practically all cotton and corn territories.

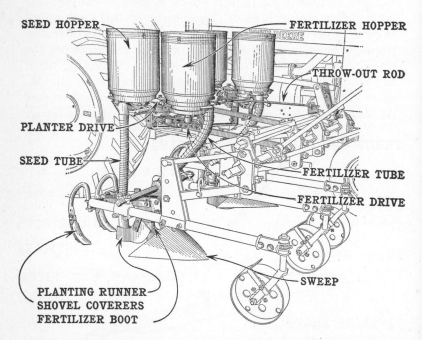

SEED HOPPER

FERTILIZER HOPPER

THROW-OUT ROD

PLANTER DRIVE

SEED TUBE

FERTILIZER TUBE

FERTILIZER DRIVE

PLANTING RUNNER
SHOVEL COVERERS
FERTILIZER BOOT

SWEEP

Figure 109—Detail illustration of planting and fertilizing equipment attached to the tractor cultivator. This equipment is available in various types to meet territorial requirements.

Planting Devices. Like corn planters, the success of combination cotton and corn planters depends upon the accuracy of the drop and its proper adjustment. The dropping device for all combination cotton and corn planters shown is the same.

The corn drop is the same as that shown, in Fig. 100, for the corn planter. Distance of drilling is regulated by the number of cells in the seed plate in all except the two-row planter, shown in Fig. 108, which has, in addition, the variable-drop control, described in the discussion of corn planters in the preceding pages, and sprockets of various sizes for the drive chain. The selection of seed plates that suit the size of seed to

Figure 110—Cotton picker wheel showing how wheel picks out cotton seed one at a time. Quantity planted per acre is controlled by turning thumb nut.

be planted is one of the most important factors in getting an even stand of corn. Fig. 98 illustrates this point.

Cotton seed is one of the most difficult of all seeds to plant accurately. For that and other reasons, it is usually planted thicker than required and the weaker plants chopped out. However, the grower wants as great a degree of accuracy as possible, and he needs to know how to adjust his planter to get best results. In unusually weedy conditions, many farmers prefer to check their cotton to permit cross-cultivation. Certain check-row planters give very good results even with undelinted cotton seed. Checking or hill-dropping cotton saves seed and reduces chopping.

The saw-tooth type steel cotton picker wheel, shown in Fig. 110, picks out the cotton seeds, one or more at a time, taking lint and trash from the hopper with the seed, and plants any quantity per acre desired. Fig. 113 shows a cross-sectional view of the hopper bottom with the cotton plate or spider in position. The spider revolves in an opposite direction to the picker wheel and delivers the seed in position for the teeth of the wheel to pick it out.

The cotton feed gate controls the amount of seed to be planted. Turning the thumb nut (see Fig. 110) to right or left increases or decreases the number of seeds picked out by the picker wheel.

Figure 111 — Planting on the contour with planting and fertilizing equipment mounted on the tractor cultivator.

The uncertainty of weather favorable to germination and growth of seed has always been one of the cotton growers' greatest concerns at planting time, for, if dry weather follows shallow planting, seed does not germinate; if wet weather follows deep planting, seed is apt to rot in the ground. Under either of these conditions, replanting, necessitating a duplication of the previous time and labor expenditure, is necessary.

The advent of a variable depth attachment for cotton planters (Fig. 112) has made possible the planting of cotton seed at depths varying uniformly from surface planting to approximately two inches. The complete cycle of depth variations is repeated every thirteen inches. This method of planting eliminates much of the uncertainty for, regardless of the weather, some seed is planted at proper depth for good germination and healthy growth. Since the cycle of variation is repeated at regular intervals, the healthiest plants are always spaced uniformly.

Changing Plates. To change from cotton to corn planting, remove thumb nut that holds the cotton spider, remove the spider, and insert the corn plate and cut-off. No other adjustment is needed. Reverse the procedure when changing from corn to cotton.

Practically all types of combination cotton and corn planters can be used for planting other row-crops such as peanuts, kafir corn, etc., by using the proper-sized plates. Several types of planters are also adapted to sowing fertilizer at the time seed is planted.

Caring for Planters. To insure good work and accurate planting, planters must be well oiled and all parts must be firmly in position. Parts must be replaced when badly worn, or the efficiency of the planter will be impaired.

Figure 112—Schematic drawing showing seed placement when the variable depth attachment is used in planting cotton. Overhead view at left above shows the two disks which revolve in unison to open a furrow of varying depth.

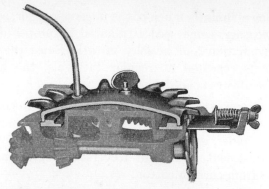

Figure 113—Cross-section of hopper bottom showing
cotton plate and picker wheel in position.

Oil holes in a new planter should be filled with kerosene to cut out the paint, after which a good grade of machine oil should be used liberally on all friction parts with the exception of parts which are enclosed in housings and operate in a constant bath of oil inside the gear case. The gear case or housing in which these parts are enclosed should be filled to the level of the oil plug with clean, new oil of viscosity recommended by the manufacturer of your planter. Inspect the oil level occasionally and if low, add sufficient new oil to fill gear case to proper level. Before the planting season opens, remove drain plug from bottom of gear case, drain old oil, and flush out with kerosene. Refill housing to proper level with clean oil. Frequent oiling adds to the life of a planter except in extremely dusty conditions when it is better to use only kerosene on all working parts, excepting, of course, parts enclosed in housing.

The entire planter should be inspected carefully for broken or badly worn parts which should be replaced before the planter is put into use. Since proper adjustment is so important to proper operation it is especially wise to check all parts for alignment and to be sure all nuts are drawn tight.

When planting in wet or sticky soils, the operator should keep close watch to see that the seed boots do not become clogged with dirt which will stop the seed from reaching bottom of the furrow. It is a good plan to inspect the boots and the entire dropping mechanism at regular intervals to see that parts are working properly.

Questions

1. *What results when row-crops are planted too thick? Too thin?*

2. *What is considered the proper number of kernels of corn to plant in a hill in your community? If corn is drilled, what distance is considered best?*

3. *Name and describe the action of the two types of corn drops.*

4. *Describe the high-speed planter valve.*

5. *What test would you make in determining the size of seed plate to use?*

6. *What special equipment or attachments are used on corn planters in your community?*

7. *Describe several types of combination cotton and corn planters and state the advantages of each. With which type are you most familiar?*

8. *Why is cotton seed difficult to plant and how does the steel saw-tooth picker wheel overcome this difficulty?*

9. *How is the quantity of seed sown regulated?*

10. *What are the advantages of planting and fertilizing equipment for cultivators?*

11. *What are the important points to remember in caring for a corn planter?*

Chapter VII.

LISTERS

Listing is a method of raising corn or other row-crops in regions having limited rainfall. Its advantages under these conditions are many. Planting the crops in the bottom of the furrow, then filling in the furrow by cultivating, keeps the plant roots deep below the surface where moisture is more plentiful. The preparation of the ground, previous to listing, is not expensive. Listed crops can be easily cultivated and kept free from weeds. For this reason, a farmer can care for a larger acreage of listed than of surface-planted row-crops.

Single listing consists of planting the crop when the ground is listed for the first time.

Blank listing is listing the seedbed without planting, an operation in which the listing plow (or lister with seeding drives disconnected and with coverers removed) is used, leaving the planting to be done with a regular corn planter or with the lister when double listing.

Double listing is the practice of blank listing in the fall to

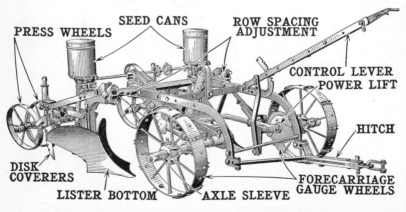

Figure 114—Two-row tractor-drawn lister with important parts named.

catch snow and hold the moisture, and splitting out the ridges and single listing in the spring.

Types of Listers. Because of the fact that the lister combines the duties of the plow and the planter, its selection as to type is important. Consideration should be given to style of bottom and coverers and to the size most practical for the acreage to be worked.

The two-row lister, shown in Fig. 114, is a modern type tractor-drawn two-row size which will be discussed in detail in a later paragraph.

The integral lister, illustrated in Fig. 115, is favored among owners of general purpose tractors since it makes up a compact outfit with the tractor. The power lift of the tractor, operated by the tractor engine, furnishes power for raising and lowering the lister.

Bottoms and Planting Equipment. The planting efficiency of a lister depends upon its bottoms and seed-dropping devices. The bottom, the subsoiler, and the

Figure 115—The integral lister makes up a compact plowing and planting outfit with the general purpose tractor.

coverers are responsible for the entire job of preparing the seedbed and covering the seed. The dropping devices determine the accuracy of planting and the spacing of the seed. When these two units are in proper adjustment, the operator can expect to do a good job of listing.

The duties of the lister bottom are similar to those of the plow bottom. It opens the seedbed, turning a furrow each way and pulverizing the soil in the same manner as does the plow. The quality of its work is even more important than in the case of the plow, as it is usually the only equipment used to prepare the soil for planting.

To do a good job, the lister bottom must be of proper shape, its share must be sharp and properly set, and its surface well polished for good scouring. When the share is sharpened, it is important that the wings be set alike. If not set the same, one side will cut deeper than the other and cause the lister to run to one side and pull heavier. To obtain proper penetration in all conditions, the share point should have approximately the same amount of underpoint suction as a plowshare.

Figure 116—Blank listing with a three-bottom integral lister.

The planting mechanism used on the listers illustrated is the same as used on the corn planters and combination cotton and corn planters described in preceding chapters. The corn drop is the same as that shown in Fig. 101. The sawtooth steel picker wheel, illustrated in Fig. 110, is used for cotton planting. Special plates for planting any row-crop can be obtained.

The importance of selecting seed plates with cells of proper size to suit the seed to be planted cannot be overemphasized. See Fig. 102, which shows how to select plate with proper-sized cells.

The seed plate and drive sprockets control the planting distance when planting crops other than cotton. The distance at which seed is planted varies with the number of cells in the seed plate used and the size of sprocket. The lister operator can select plates and sprockets to space the seed the desired distance in the drilled rows.

Field Adjustments. The tractor-drawn lister, shown in Fig. 114, is a typical two-row lister in general use. It is fully adaptable to listing requirements and is easily adjustable for row-spacing desired. Both listing units are mounted by clamps to a common frame bar along which they are easily shifted to proper spacing. Front wheels serve the double purpose of forecarriage to support the front of the lister and gauge wheels to maintain uniform depth of tilling and planting. A single long lever serves as master lever to vary the depth of plowing and planting. The power lift unit in the left-hand wheel raises the lister. Press wheels at the rear firm the soil in the trench over the seed. Principal parts of the lister are indicated in the illustration.

On the two- and three-row listers, rows can be spaced at various distances apart by moving the hitch, bottoms, cans, and wheels in or out by means of the adjustments provided. The operator must be sure to move each the same distance so that all will be in line to plant rows of uniform width.

The subsoiler opens the seed trench. It should not be set deeper than necessary to do proper work—about one and one-half inches below the point of the share.

When rolling coulter is used, it must be set in line with the exact center of the bottom, or one furrow will be wider than the other, resulting in uneven work and side draft.

Covering disks or shovels must be set alike, or they will lead the lister to one side.

Rear wheels must run straight. The lock casting on the upright angle below frame casting must be kept straight so that wheels run parallel to each other. Wheels may be staggered in or out to meet soil conditions by reversing the axle.

Care of Listers. Length of service and working qualities of a lister depend greatly upon the care given it. All polished parts—bottoms, subsoilers, root cutters, and coverers—should be coated with oil whenever the lister is not in use. Rust pits on these parts prevent scouring and hinder good work. Disk coverers, wheel boxings, and all points of friction should be oiled regularly.

General overhauling after each planting season, with special attention to worn and loose parts, will add to the life of the lister.

Questions

1. What is the purpose and what are the advantages of listing crops?
2. What is single listing? Blank listing? Double listing?
3. Describe several types of listers.
4. Why are the bottoms of first importance to good work in a lister?
5. How is planting distance controlled?
6. How is row-spacing controlled on two- and three-row listers?
7. What is the purpose of the master lever? Leveling lever?
8. What are the important points in caring for a lister?

Chapter VIII.

POTATO PLANTERS

Growing potatoes for market without modern equipment for planting and harvesting them is an expensive and laborious task. The slow, difficult hand-drop method of planting has been supplanted to a great extent by mechanical planters that open a furrow, space the seed at the desired distance, and cover it at the proper depth. Mechanical diggers that remove and separate the potatoes from the soil and vines do away with the slow, tiresome practice of plowing out the crop with an ordinary plow.

The potato planter is in quite common use in most sections of the country even where comparatively small acreages are planted. It has been an important factor in making potatoes a profitable crop—one that ranks high in value among the leading crops. Lower production costs, due to saving time and labor, and bigger yields because of uniform planting and

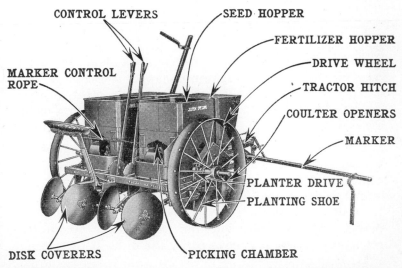

Figure 117—Two-row tractor potato planter with important parts indicated.

covering, are two advantages derived from the use of a potato planter.

Types of Planters. The type of potato planter in common use is illustrated in Fig. 117. It is well adapted to planting conditions in practically every potato-growing section. A fertilizer attachment that deposits fertilizer on each side of the furrow and mixes it properly with the soil can be added, making a two-purpose machine that is both practical and economical.

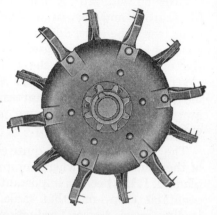

Figure 118—The tractor planter is equipped with 12 picker points to insure effective, accurate planting at tractor speed.

When potatoes are raised on a large scale, two-row planters of this type are used with a big saving in time and production costs.

Principle of Operation. Potato planters of the one-man, or picker type, shown in Fig. 117, have often been described as "almost human" in their work of picking out a piece of seed and dropping it in its proper place. Their work is more difficult probably than that of any other planting machine because of the irregularity in size and shape of the seed they are required to plant.

The picker wheel is shown in Fig. 118. Picker arms, revolving on the main axle, pass through the picking chamber containing the seed. Each picker arm is equipped with two sharp picking points which pick out one piece of seed. As the arm passes downward, the seed is forced off the picker points. The seed drops into the trench made by the furrow opener where it is covered by the disks at the rear.

Adjustments are provided to meet planting conditions

encountered in any section of the country and under varying field and seed conditions.

Proper Feeding Necessary. One of the important requirements for accurate planting is the maintenance of the

Figure 119—The two-row tractor planter speeds the work of planting on many large farms.

proper amount of seed in the picking chamber. In the planter illustrated, the gravity feed, with automatic control, provides a constant flow of seed from hopper to picking chamber.

When the seed in the picking chamber reaches a given level which provides about the right quantity of seed for efficient performance, no more seed will flow into the picking chamber except as required to replace seed planted.

One lever controls opener and disk coverers of each unit on the planter shown in Fig. 117. When these parts are lowered with the lever, the machine is placed in gear automatically. The disk coverers are adjustable for covering at the desired depth.

Spacing of the seed in the row is dependent upon the size of sprocket wheel used on the intermediate shaft. Changing from one spacing to another is a simple operation.

Care Lengthens Life. Like all other machines, the potato planter will last longer and give more satisfactory service if it is oiled properly when in use and when stored. A thorough overhauling before each planting season will add to its efficiency and life.

Questions

1. *What are the advantages of using a potato planter?*
2. *What types of potato planters are used in your community?*
3. *Describe the principle of operation of the potato planter.*
4. *Why is proper feeding necessary?*
5. *Describe, in general, the operation of a potato planter.*

Part Four

CULTIVATING

Proper cultivation of row-crops during the growing season has much to do with the yield and the quality of the crop produced. This fact is apparent to anyone who has observed the results of good cultivation and of poor cultivation in adjacent fields. Corn, potatoes, or any other crop that is smothered by weeds will produce little compared with the well-cultivated crop.

The destruction of weeds is the primary purpose of cultivation. Weeds draw moisture and plant food from the soil, robbing the growing crop. Weeds are truly thieves in the fields; they steal profits when permitted to grow unhampered.

Cultivation serves two other purposes as well. It creates a moisture-saving surface mulch and admits air and light to

Figure 120—Cultivating speeds up when the tractor cultivator takes over this important job.

the soil. If the soil becomes crusted after a rain, it should be broken into a mulch to prevent the escape of moisture through capillary attraction. Air and light are essentials to plant growth and are admitted to the soil more readily when the surface is loose and ridged.

The first requirement of a cultivator is that it be quickly and easily adaptable to varying field conditions. The operator will find it impossible to cut out all the weeds and stir the ground evenly unless his cultivator is adjusted properly. Angle of the shovels, tilt of the rig beams, depth of each rig, and setting of pole (on horse-drawn cultivators) must be correct for efficient work. Quick, easy adaptability to all conditions is the most valuable attribute of a cultivator.

Chapter IX.

ROTARY HOES

Although not strictly a cultivator, the rotary hoe must be classed as a cultivator because of the work it does. Its main purpose is to destroy weeds and create a surface mulch.

The rotary hoe has proved itself of considerable value when used in the early stages of crop growth, this being especially true in corn and other row-crops. It is also used with success in small grain crops and in any condition where it is desired to break up a crusted surface soil. It is used to best advantage after heavy rains have packed the ground and created an unsatisfactory surface tilth.

Hoe Teeth Stir Soil. The rotary hoe is made up of two series of hoe wheels, one series mounted on the front gang axle and the other on the rear gang axle, spaced so the rear wheels work the soil left between the front wheels. Each hoe wheel has 16 teeth, shaped like fingers, which penetrate and stir the soil as the wheels rotate. A thoroughly-pulverized surface results; weeds are uprooted and the soil is left in good condition for plant growth.

While its work is most satisfactory when crops are just coming through the ground, the rotary hoe is used to good advantage in stimulating the growth of crops after they have passed this stage. Some farmers report satisfactory results using a rotary hoe in corn that has reached a height of ten inches.

Three sizes of rotary hoes are in general use—the two-row, the four-row shown in Fig. 121, and the six-row. The larger sizes are probably more economical for the average farmer because of their greater capacity. On large farms, where extra capacity is desired, the practice of operating special hook-ups of two or three rotary hoes behind the tractor is growing in popularity. Special hitches for this purpose are furnished by the manufacturer.

Easy to Operate. The rotary hoe is easy to operate and adjust. Once the machine has been set at the proper depth, the operator has little to do but drive his team or tractor.

Figure 121—The four-row rotary hoe working in small corn.

Questions

1. *Describe the action of a rotary hoe.*
2. *Under what conditions do rotary hoes do the best work?*
3. *What crops are cultivated with rotary hoes in your community?*
4. *What sizes of rotary hoes are in common use in your community and which is most popular? Why?*

Chapter X.

SHOVEL CULTIVATORS

Shovel cultivators are the most generally-used type in the majority of farming communities, since they are suited to practically all soils and to average conditions. They are available with a wide variety of shovel equipment for thorough work in all crops and soils.

Horse-Drawn Cultivators. A typical horse-drawn cultivator is shown in Fig. 122. Levers are provided to make all field adjustments. The master lever raises all rigs. Independent depth levers raise or lower each rig separately, permitting adjustment for good work in uneven ground. Spacing lever moves shovels closer to or farther from the rows, giving operator instant control of spacing while cultivator is at work. The tilting lever levels rigs, causing front

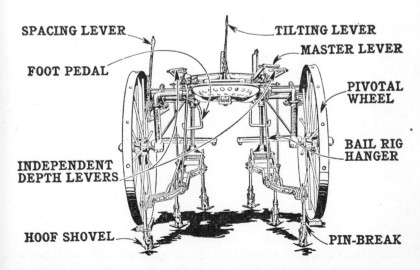

Figure 122—One-row riding cultivator of the parallel rig, lever shift type.

and rear shovels to run at same depth when going uphill or downhill or on uneven ground.

The swinging rig type of cultivator, shown in Fig. 123, is a style of walking cultivator in common use. It is adjusted for spacing and cultivating closer to or farther from the row, by loosening the arches and sliding them in or out to width desired.

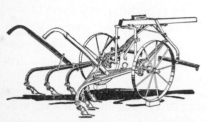

Figure 123—One-row walking cultivator.

Operation and Adjustment. When a cultivator is set properly for working in ordinary conditions, all shovels will penetrate well, run at the same depth without crowding toward or away from the row, and there will be no unnecessary draft. To set and maintain a cultivator in this desirable adjustment is comparatively easy, once the operator understands the causes of trouble and the adjustments provided on his cultivator for correcting them.

One of the most common adjustments that cultivator operators have to make is setting the shovels for proper penetration and uniform depth. The first requirement of an efficient shovel is that it be sharp, with the point properly shaped. A dull shovel will not penetrate easily; it does poor work and causes heavier draft. Fig. 124 shows a properly-shaped shovel with a dotted line showing its shape when point is worn and dull. Frequent sharpening of shovels will insure a smooth-running, good-working cultivator.

All shovels must run at the same depth for good work. If the front shovels run deeper than the rear ones, all shovels will stand straighter than they should and will not penetrate easily. This condition is due to the front of rigs being lower than the rear. It can be corrected by raising the pole at hames or leveling the rigs with the tilting or leveling lever.

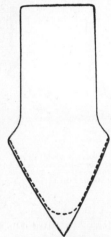

Figure 124—Cultivator shovel with dotted lines showing how point looks when shovel needs resharpening. Obviously, a shovel in this condition penetrates poorly and increases draft.

If the rear shovels run deeper than those in front, all shovels set too flat and will not penetrate as they should. This can be remedied with the tilting lever on some types of cultivators and with adjustment at the hames on types that do not have such a lever. These directions are based upon the supposition, of course, that all shovels are at uniform height on the shanks.

Pitch of Shovels. All cultivators are provided with an adjustment, either on the shovel shank or sleeve, whereby the pitch or angle of the shovel can be changed. This adjustment is correct for average soil conditions when the cultivator leaves the factory. However, it may become changed and it is well to know what the proper pitch is and how to get it when conditions demand.

If a shovel stands too straight, it will not penetrate readily; it will not run steadily. There will be a tendency to skip and jump, and it will require unusual pressure to keep the shovels at work. If set too flat, the underpart of the shovel will ride below the extreme point and the shovel will not penetrate unless forced into the ground.

The illustrations in Fig. 125 show the proper pitch of shovels for good work compared with shovels set too straight and too slanting.

In hilling row-crops, it is necessary to turn the front shovels in by loosening the clamp attachment on the shank. This setting tends to pull the shovels away from the row. This tendency does not interfere with the work of a pivot axle cultivator, but with the swinging rig type; the operator finds difficulty in keeping the rigs running the proper distance from the row when spread arch is not used. An opposite effect is produced when the front shovels are turned away from the row for first cultivation. In either case, the crowding tendency can be overcome and the rigs made to run straight

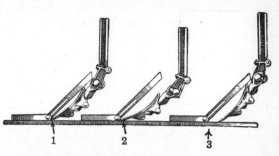

Figure 125—Showing correct and incorrect pitch of cultivator shovels. No. 1, shovel properly adjusted; No. 2, shovel set too flat. will not penetrate well; No. 3, shovel set too straight, will not penetrate or run steadily.

by turning the rear shovels to an equal angle in the opposite direction. On parallel rig types of cultivators, turning the shovels in or out does not affect the operation of the cultivator.

The wheel tread is adjustable on most types of cultivators. This is an important feature in districts where several widths of rows must be cultivated with the same machines. The cultivators shown can be adjusted to several different row-widths by removing a cotter key or loosening a set screw and moving axles in or out an equal distance to the desired position. Other types of cultivators are adjusted in a similar manner.

Adjustment of Shields. Proper setting of the shields is important to good work during the first cultivation. There are three main types used—solid sheet steel, open rod wire, and rotating. With the first type, which is the most commonly used, it is comparatively easy to make the proper setting which will allow the desired amount of dirt to roll up to the row without covering the plants. The rotating shield is often set too far back to be efficient. The greater part of the shield should be ahead of the front shovel, with its entire weight resting on the ground. For later cultivation, shields are removed, provided the crop has reached sufficient height.

Care of Cultivators. Like all other farm implements, the length of life and the satisfaction given by shovel cultivators depend upon the way they are handled and the care given them during operation and storage. A few minutes given to inspection and tightening of all parts, and thorough oiling at regular intervals while in the field will add to the service of a cultivator and save delays caused by breakage and wear. Shovels should be polished and coated with oil when standing overnight and covered thoroughly with heavy grease when stored.

As stated previously, one of the most important factors in efficient cultivation is keeping the shovels sharp. A dull shovel is as inefficient as a dull knife. It is advisable to have the shovels sharpened and shaped by a good blacksmith during the storage season. If the points are too badly worn, new shovels or new points (for the slip-point type of shovel) should be obtained. If the shovels have become rusted and pitted between seasons, they should be polished before being taken into the field.

It is advisable to go over the cultivator thoroughly, during the slack season, ordering new parts wherever needed and tuning it up ready for the first day of the cultivating season.

Questions

1. What are the purposes of cultivation?
2. What are the requirements of a good cultivator?
3. What conditions govern the type of rig equipment used? What type is used in your community?
4. Why is it important that cultivator shovels be kept sharp?
5. What causes front shovels to run deeper than rear ones? How corrected?
6. What relation has the pitch of a cultivator shovel to its work?
7. How would you set shovels to cause the rigs to run straight when hilling?
8. What is the advantage of an adjustable wheel tread?
9. Of what value are shields and how are they adjusted?
10. Tell how you would care for a shovel cultivator when in use and when placed in storage.

128

Tractor Cultivators

Its adaptability to cultivating row-crops is one of the chief reasons for the broad acceptance of the general purpose type of tractor especially in territories where row-crops predominate. Field experience has proved that tractor cultivators effect great savings in time and labor. The steady speed of a tractor cannot be matched by horses, especially on hot days. And, too, the speed can be controlled to meet crop and field conditions to best advantage.

Owners of tractor cultivators find they can put in more hours per day in the field—cultivating capacity is not limited by the endurance of animal power. In rush seasons, cultivating can be finished sooner, and the time saved can be utilized in taking care of other crops. When the weather is unsettled, the owner of a tractor cultivator can take full advantage of favorable conditions.

Operation and Care. The two-row tractor cultivator, shown in Fig. 126, is adapted to use in crops planted with

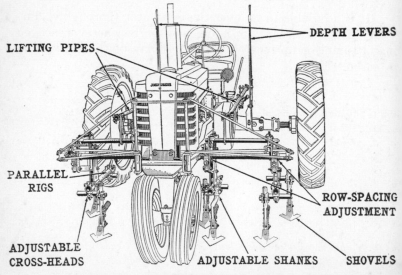

Figure 126—Two-row tractor cultivator mounted on general purpose adjustable-tread type of tractor.

two- or four-row tractor planters. The four-row cultivator, illustrated in Fig. 127, is used in cultivating row-crops planted with four-row planters. A special cultivator for use in narrow row-crops is shown in Fig. 32. These cultivators form a single unit with the tractors and are controlled entirely from the tractor seat. The entire unit steers with the tractor—once the equipment is properly set, the operator's only duty is steering the tractor and setting the power lift into action or pulling the lift lever at the row-ends.

The entire cultivator is removed without disturbing row-spacing or other adjustments and may be kept in shed or lot as a complete unit, ready for work. To attach, the operator simply drives into the cultivator unit until the side frame bars are snug against the tractor frame. A single bolt holds each side of the unit to the tractor.

The frame of the four-row cultivator is rigid, flexibility being obtained through the floating construction of the rigs. The depth of cultivating is automatically controlled by individual gauge wheels, the rigs following the contour of the field as the tractor moves along.

Figure 127—Four-row tractor cultivator on a general-purpose adjustable-tread tractor. This big-capacity type outfit is becoming more popular each year.

When the operator reaches the end of the field with the power-lifted cultivator, he touches a pedal which sets the power lift into action. The power lift raises all the rigs—the turn is made without stopping—the operator touches the pedal again and the rigs are lowered to work.

The shovels used on the tractor cultivators, shown here, are practically the same in design as those described in connection with the horse-drawn cultivators on preceding pages with exception, of course, that they are built with extra strength for tractor power. They should be adjusted and cared for in the same manner as other cultivator shovels. Spring trips protect the shovels and shanks against breakage. On the spring-tooth type cultivator, popular in many sections, the spring teeth act as the safety factor to protect cultivator from breakage.

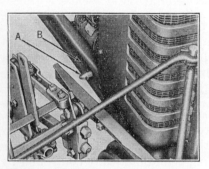

Figure 128—Cultivator side frame bar slips over pilot pin (A) and is held securely by a bolt through tractor frame and cultivator side frame bar at (B).

Careful adjustment and thorough oiling of cultivating equipment will increase the efficiency and lengthen the life of tractor cultivators.

Questions

1. What are some of the advantages of owning a tractor cultivator?
2. How is the cultivator guided?
3. Why is it necessary that a tractor cultivator have flexibility?
4. How is the cultivating equipment, on the cultivators illustrated, raised and lowered?
5. How would you adjust depth of each rig, individually; all rigs at one time?

Part Five

HARVESTING

Harvest season is the busiest time of the year on every farm. All hands are turned to gathering the returns of the year's work. Grain, hay, food crops, and fruits must be harvested at the proper time if losses are to be avoided.

When the small grain is ready to be harvested, a delay of a few days may cause heavy losses. Hay must be cut, cured, and stored in the shortest possible time to retain its maximum feeding value. Fruits are ripe and must be picked for the market. All forces should work in harmony at the harvest.

Then, too, farm machines must be at their highest state of efficiency. Combines, binders, threshers, mowers, rakes, pickers, and all other machines must be tuned up in advance for speed and good work. The operator must know how to make adjustments and repairs to get the most from his machines. He should be familiar with causes of inefficiency and know how to correct them with a minimum of effort and time.

Harvesting machines are probably the most intricate of all to adjust and operate. However, once the operator knows his machine and the adjustments that must be made most often, efficiency is maintained with little difficulty. The most common causes of trouble in harvesting machinery can be avoided by thorough and regular oiling, by replacing worn parts before they affect the machine's operation, and by an occasional complete overhauling and adjustment of parts.

Chapter XI.

GRAIN BINDERS

Since the introduction of the reaper and the first self-binder, steady advancement has been made in binder design. The binders on the market today, for the most part, are built to a high degree of perfection in the essentials necessary to good harvesting.

Types of Binders. Grain binders may be classified as horse-drawn, (Fig. 131) which take power for the cutting operation and binding mechanism direct from the bull wheel of the machine; and tractor binders, (Fig. 130) power for the operation of which is taken from the power take-off of the tractor.

The mechanism of tractor binders is driven direct from the tractor by power transmitted through a power drive shaft (see Fig. 130). The main or bull wheel of the binder merely carries the weight. This results in steady, even operation of the binder in all conditions—wet ground, loose ground, and down or tangled grain do not cause delays or interfere with good work as might be the case with horse-drawn binders.

Figure 129—Cutting and binding with the tractor binder.

In unusually heavy grain, the forward speed of the tractor can be reduced while the speed of the binder mechanism is maintained. Thus, heavy crops can be handled with a minimum of clogging or stopping.

Levers that can be handled from the tractor seat are obtainable for most tractor binders. This permits one man to operate both the tractor and binder. Equipment for controlling the tractor from the binder seat is available also.

Since the general operating instructions for both tractor- and horse-drawn binders are much the same, the discussion of grain binders will center around the machine shown in Fig. 131.

For harvesting rice, a special binder is needed because of the wet and ridged condition that usually exists in the fields at harvest time. Fig. 133 shows a rice binder, the operation and care of which are essentially the same as the horse-drawn grain binder. This binder is operated by tractor power, but can be obtained for use with horses as well.

Oiling of First Importance. There is probably no other farm machine that requires more thorough and regular oiling

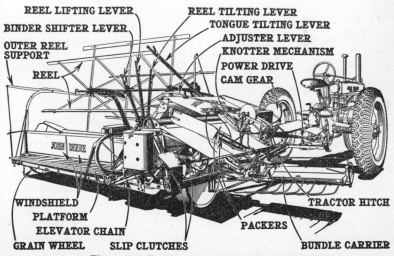

Figure 130—Tractor binder with tractor attached.

than the grain binder. Its draft, efficiency, and length of life depend greatly upon the liberal use of good, heavy machine oil on all bearings and working parts.

Manufacturers are constantly striving to build their binders with oil holes, cups, plugs, and grease fittings more accessible to the operator. The binders, shown in Figs. 130, 131, and 133, are equipped with a high-pressure grease gun oiling system, making thorough oiling an easy job.

The main drive gears, which transfer power from the bull wheel for operating the horse-drawn binder, are completely encased and operate in grease, as shown in Fig. 132. An occasional check to maintain level of grease in the housing is all that is necessary to keep the main drive gears lubricated properly.

Setting Levers for Good Work. Efficient operation of a grain binder requires the proper setting of all levers to meet all field conditions to best advantage. Poorly-shaped bundles, scattering of grain, and heavy draft are often caused by failure to make proper use of the levers. There is usually

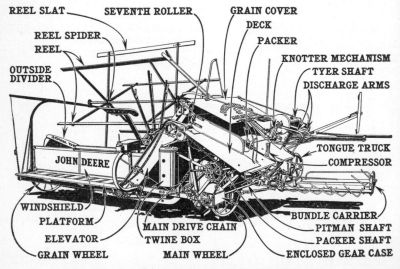

Figure 131—The horse-drawn ground-driven grain binder.

a real necessity for making frequent lever adjustments in even the best of field conditions.

The raising and lowering devices on the main and grain wheels, which set the platform higher or lower, together with the tilting lever and the adjustable tongue tilting connection straps, provide a wide range of adjustment for cutting stubble high or low, and for tilting the platform to the necessary angle. These adjustments are found on all binders, yet they are used to best advantage by few binder operators.

The tilting lever controls the forward and backward tilt of the binder. For ordinary cutting, it should be set so that the binder platform tilts slightly forward. When cutting lodged or tangled grain, the machine should be tilted low to get as many of the heads as possible. If it is necessary to tilt the platform in this manner, the binder should be raised a little more than halfway on the main wheel and grain wheel hangers.

The purpose of the reel is to tip the cut grain onto the platform canvas as evenly as possible, in position to make neat bundles. Reel levers provide a wide range of adjustment for setting the reel for good work. Under normal conditions, the reel slats should touch the grain close to the heads and leave the grain just after it is cut off. If there is

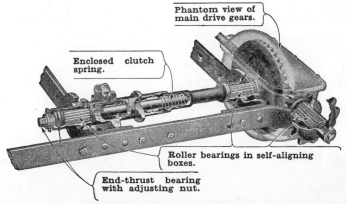

Figure 132—Detail of main drive gears.

a strong wind, it will be necessary to make test adjustments to see in which position the reel will do the best job of placing the grain evenly on the canvas. In lodged grain, the reel is set low and forward to aid in getting more of the down heads and straw.

The adjuster lever controls the position of the butter. The butter should be run as far forward as possible so that the grain is not forced backward from its line of travel as it comes up between the elevator canvases. In very short grain, it may be necessary to shift the adjuster back in order to place the band near the center of the bundle. Otherwise, the adjuster lever should not be used for regulating placing of the band.

Shifting the binder attachment with the binder shifter lever regulates the position of the twine on the bundle. It should be placed near the center of the bundle in grain of any height. It may be necessary to shift the binder with the binder shifter lever several times in making a round if the grain is of uneven height. This adjustment should be made as often as necessary to make uniform, well-tied bundles.

The platform grain shield and the windboard at rear of the binder deck will assist in making better bundles and prevent scattering of grain if properly adjusted for long or short straw.

Adjustment of Chains, Canvases. For best results, all chains should be run just tight enough to do the work. Draft and wear are increased materially by having them

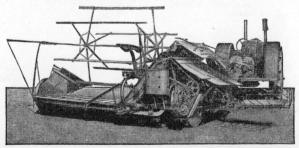

Figure 133—Tractor rice binder.

too tight; if the chains are run too loose, they will climb the sprockets, break links, and wear the chain or sprockets rapidly. A loose main wheel chain is very often the cause of the binder's choking.

An occasional oiling lengthens the life of chains.

Fig. 134 illustrates the proper method of attaching a chain on a sprocket and the best way to detach a chain.

Canvases should be run just tight enough to do their work of carrying the grain to the binding unit. If run too tight, wear and draft are increased materially. When a canvas is put on, all straps must be adjusted the same or the canvas will not run straight. The roller bearings on the elevator rollers that carry the canvases should be oiled regularly, as a sluggish roller increases draft and may cause clogging.

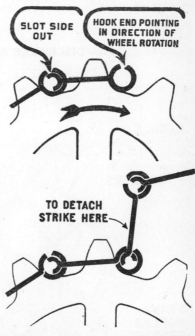

Binding Attachment Adjustments. The binding attachment is adjusted properly when the binder leaves the factory, and will operate successfully under average conditions without adjusting. It is a good plan to make no such adjustments on a new binder until the paint is worn off the working parts and they become smooth. However, when it becomes apparent that an adjustment will be necessary to insure efficient

Figure 134—For best results, put chains on sprockets as shown in the upper illustration. Lower illustration shows how to detach a chain: using a tooth of the wheel for a brace, bend to the position shown, and strike the link at the point indicated by arrow.

work, the operator should determine where the trouble exists before tampering with the parts of the binding attachment. If knotter or twine tension adjustments are made and do not correct the trouble, they should be changed back to their original position.

Frequently a few drops of oil will correct a difficulty that appears to be serious. A loose nut may cause trouble beyond estimate. The shrewd binder operator will look for small troubles first, before attempting to make major adjustments of the binding attachment.

The illustrations in Figs. 136, 137, 138, and 139 show how the knot is tied. Careful study of this process will aid in a better understanding of the principles of binder operation.

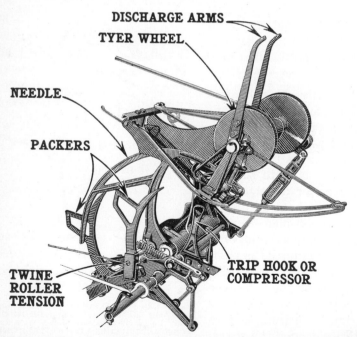

Figure 135—View of the binding unit with some of the parts named and indicated by arrows.

Twine Tension. Incorrect twine tension is one of the most common causes of missed bundles. The twine should furnish a resistance of from six to eight pounds at the point of the needle. This is necessary to prevent slack interfering with the operation of the tying parts.

Twine tension is determined in the following manner: thread the machine with the exception of bringing the needle over to get the twine in the disk; tie a loop in the twine under the breastplate, hook a fifty-pound spring balance or draw scale into the loop and pull the twine through the needle eye, pulling on a line parallel with the binder deck. The scale should register between six and eight pounds if proper tension has been created.

The twine roller spring under the binder deck (see Fig. 135) controls the tension of the twine and is adjusted by loosening or tightening the tension spring. The spring should have free action and the rollers should turn freely with the pull of the twine if the tension test is to be accurate. This adjustment does not affect the tension of the band around the bundle; the trip stop spring affords adjustment for this purpose.

Trip Tension. To determine the number of pounds required to trip the binder and start the tying process, hook a scale into the upper end of the trip hook (see Fig. 135) and pull in a line parallel to the discharge arms when they have completed the discharge of a bundle. The tension should be twenty to twenty-two pounds.

The tension of the trip hook determines the tension of the twine around the bundle. If it is desired to increase or decrease this tension, the trip stop spring (Fig. 140) is adjusted accordingly.

Size of bundle is controlled by adjusting the trip hook in or out on the trip hook arm. If small bundles are desired, the trip hook is set closer to the needle and the trip stop spring is

Figure 136—Binder has been tripped and needle has advanced, bringing twine around bundle and placing second strand over knotter jaw and into disk notch.

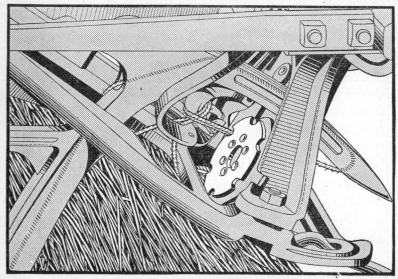

Figure 137—Disk has advanced and grasped both strands of twine. Knotter hook has turned, forming a loop of twine around the hook, and jaw has opened to receive twine leading to disk.

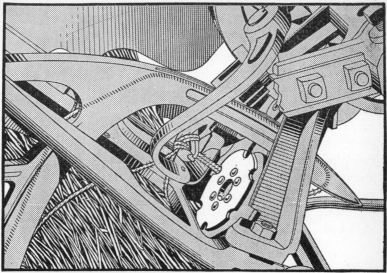

Figure 138—Knotter jaw has closed, holding twine tightly. Knife is advancing, ready to cut twine between knotter hook and disk.

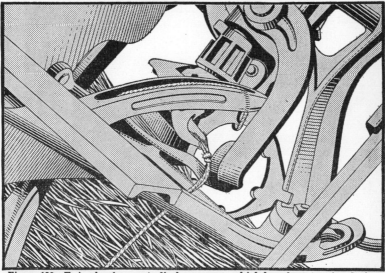

Figure 139—Twine has been cut; discharge arms, which have been turning during tying operation, strike bundle as twine is cut, assisting knife arm to strip loop from knotter hook. Knotter jaw holds ends while loop is slipped off, making complete and secure knot. With end of twine in disk, needle returns to home position, leaving strand of twine over knotter jaw.

loosened slightly. If large bundles are wanted, the trip hook is set out on the trip arm and the trip stop spring is tightened.

Twine Holder or Disk Tension. Perfect tying of knots is possible only when the twine holder or disk is set at the proper tension—thirty-five to forty pounds. To test this tension, thread the machine ready for tying, pull the trip hook, and turn the discharge arms one complete revolution. Take off the band and knot that were completed so as to have the twine securely in the disk. Tie a loop in the twine directly above the knotter frame, hook the scale into this loop and pull straight upward (Fig. 141). By tightening or loosening the twine holder spring (Fig. 142), the required tension is obtained.

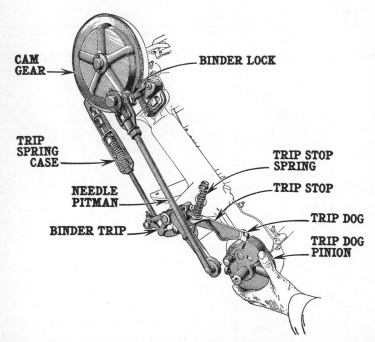

CAM GEAR

BINDER LOCK

TRIP SPRING CASE

TRIP STOP SPRING

TRIP STOP

NEEDLE PITMAN

BINDER TRIP

TRIP DOG

TRIP DOG PINION

Figure 140—Front view of the binder head. Adjust trip stop spring to tie bundles tighter or looser.

When adjusting the twine holder spring, it is necessary to loosen the lock nut before the set screw can be turned. It is advisable to give the set screw only a one-quarter turn in making a test setting. The lock nut must be tightened again after proper setting has been made.

Needle Setting. The needle and the parts that affect its operation should not be tampered with, unless it is obvious that the original settings have been changed or that wear has made an adjustment necessary.

It is the purpose of the needle to place the twine in the twine holder or disk

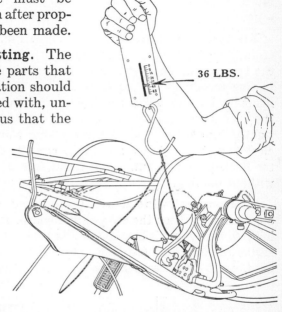

36 LBS.

Figure 141—Method of testing twine holder or disk tension.

notches (Fig. 142). To do this, when the binder is tripped and turned empty, the needle must press hard against the knife arm. The needle should also set over close to the knotter pinion when passing through knotter frame, if twine is to be placed in the disk notch properly. If it should be found necessary to advance the needle, this can be done by shortening the needle pitman (Fig. 140) one or more threads, as the case may require.

Knotter Cam. The knotter hook cam (Fig. 143) presses against the knotter tongue roller and holds the tongue closed when the knot is being completed. This is necessary to cause the two ends of the twine to be pulled through to make a complete and secure knot.

Pressure of the cam against the knotter tongue roller is controlled by a coil spring. This spring is often tightened too much. It should be just tight enough to hold the knotter tongue closed when the tying process is being finished.

Knotter Frame Adjustment. (See Fig. 142.) The face of the knotter hook pinion should set up close to the face of the tyer wheel. The wear on these parts is taken up by adjusting eccentrics "A" and "B". When this is necessary to make the knotter and worm shaft pinions mesh properly with the tyer wheel, care must be taken not to crowd them too tightly into mesh. The knotter frame should be set just close enough to the tyer wheel to permit the face of the knotter hook pinion to rub against the face of the tyer wheel without binding.

Sharpening Twine Knife. For efficient work, the binder operator must keep the twine knife sharp. It needs sharpening frequently and is brought to the best cutting edge with a carborundum stone (see Fig. 147). A file should never be used, as it produces a rough edge not suitable to cutting

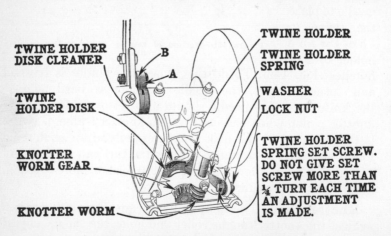

Figure 142—Close-up view of tying parts.

twine. The carborundum stone gives a keen edge that cuts easily and accurately.

Hints on Tying Troubles. When starting to locate causes of tying trouble, first examine the twine in the box to see if it is unwinding freely; then follow it through the roller

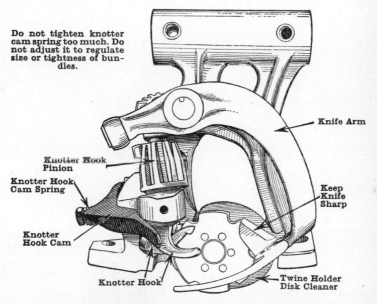

Do not tighten knotter cam spring too much. Do not adjust it to regulate size or tightness of bundles.

Knife Arm

Knotter Hook Pinion

Knotter Hook Cam Spring

Keep Knife Sharp

Knotter Hook Cam

Knotter Hook

Twine Holder Disk Cleaner

Figure 143—Close-up of knotter parts and twine-cutting knife.

tension, twine guides, needle, and disk, watching for conditions that might produce slack or too much tension. Test the twine tension, trip hook tension, and the twine holder or disk tension as directed in preceding paragraphs. Adjust very carefully where necessary.

It is well to remember that uneven, weak, wet, dried-out, or poor twine of any kind will cause missed bundles. Experience has proved that it is poor policy to buy cheap twine of doubtful quality.

Missed bundles may also be due to the condition of the straw. In heavy, tangled, tough straw, which overloads the binder, the needle may carry straws into the twine disk and

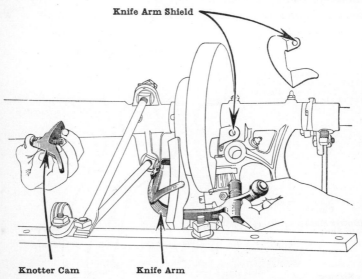

Knife Arm Shield

Knotter Cam   Knife Arm

Figure 144—To remove knife arm, remove knife arm shield, unscrew bolt and remove knotter cam, then swing knife arm out under knotter shield.

prevent the twine from entering in the proper manner. A missed bundle results.

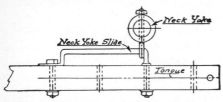

Neck Yoke

Neck Yoke Slide

Tongue

Figure 145—Neckyoke should be at front of the neckyoke slide when the team is moving forward.

This condition can be remedied to some extent by keeping the needle point sharp and the entire needle well polished, setting the grain cover down low, setting the trip hook and trip stop spring to make smaller bundles, and setting the steel breastplate flanges close to the needle.

What to Look for. Some of the usual kinds of defective bands and the cause of each are as follows:

If there is a knot in only one end of the band and the other end is cut square, as though cut off with a sharp knife, the twine holder spring is *too loose*. (See Fig. 142.) This band is usually found with the bundle.

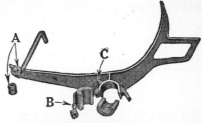

Figure 146—Packer bushings "A" and "B" are replaceable. Oil hole "C" should be filled with oil frequently.

If there is a knot in only one end, and the other end of this band is flattened out, torn, or ragged, the twine holder spring is *too tight*. This band will be found with the bundle.

If there is no knot in either end of the band, the knotter hook cam spring is *too loose*. (See Fig. 143.) This band is usually found with the bundle.

If the band is hanging on the knotter hook and is broken by the bundle being discharged, then the knotter hook cam spring is *too tight.*

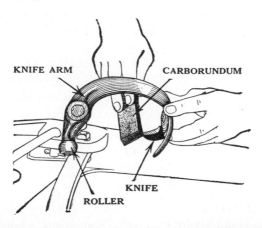

KNIFE ARM   CARBORUNDUM

ROLLER   KNIFE

Figure 147—Carborundum stone should be used for sharpening twine knife. Original bevel should be maintained.

If, in picking up a bundle with the band around the bundle, one end slips out, the disk may be slow. This happens on old knotters, due to wear. Put one or two washers just above the worm on the worm shaft to advance the disk just the amount necessary. If this defective knot is made by a new binder, the twine holder spring usually needs to be tightened slightly.

If the band is found tied in slip noose around the bundle with the twine extending from bundle to the eye of the needle, the needle has failed to place twine in the disk. If the roller at needle point is badly worn, loosen and turn half around, and then tighten it.

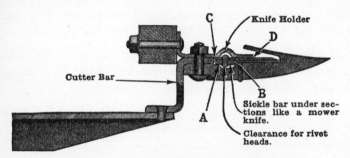

Figure 148—The sickle has a bearing along entire length of the cutter bar at "C", and on all guards at "A". The sickle is also guided by the guards at "B" and holder at "D".

Packers. The packers play an important part in making a compact, neatly-shaped bundle. If the bearings become worn, the packers wobble and are inefficient in their work, in which case new bearings should be installed.

Fig. 146 illustrates a binder packer equipped with removable bearings, oil-soaked wood bearing at "B", and tempered steel bearing at "A". This type of bearing makes replacement an easy and inexpensive operation.

Cutting Parts. A cross-section of the grain binder cutting parts is shown in Fig. 148. The details of adjustment and repair of the sickle, guards, and knife holders are practically the same as those given for the mower in a following chapter. These details may be studied, if desired, in connection with the study of the grain binder.

Point on Hitching. Binder operators sometimes experience trouble with a horse-drawn binder having a tongue truck because short hitching causes tipping of the truck in turning corners.

This difficulty can be overcome by hitching the team and adjusting the neckyoke slide bolt (Fig. 145) so that the neckyoke works to the front end of the slide when the team is going forward. When turning, the neckyoke can slide back freely on the bolt, and pole team will have more clearance for turning. If the neckyoke does not slide back, the pole team pulls back and down on the tongue when turning, causing the truck to tip. Another advantage of setting the neckyoke slide properly is that it gives the outside horse a chance to travel ahead freely without pulling up on the hitch in turning.

Careful Handling Prolongs Life. A grain binder will give more years of service if it is given more than ordinary care. Thorough oiling, keeping nuts tight, making adjust-

Figure 149—Cutting wheat with a tractor binder.

ments that take up wear, and replacing worn parts before they break are factors that lengthen the life and increase the working efficiency of a grain binder.

As soon as harvest is over and before the binder is stored it should be cleaned—all old grease, dirt, and chaff removed, and all cutting and tying parts covered with oil to prevent rust. Working parts should be examined and any found to be worn should be replaced by new parts during slack seasons. Every minute spent in tuning up a binder for the next season may mean a saving of an hour or several hours at harvest time. Fig. 149 shows a grain binder doing a good job of cutting.

Questions

1. *Name the three types of grain binders mentioned.*

2. *What are some of the advantages of a tractor binder over a horse-drawn binder?*

3. *What is of first importance in operating a grain binder?*

4. *How may the tilting lever be used to advantage in "down" grain?*

5. *What is the function of the reel and how should it be run in average conditions?*

6. *What controls the position of the twine on the bundle? Where should the twine be placed to make neat bundles?*

7. *How should the chains and canvases be run for best results?*

8. *Why should the binding attachment be tampered with as little as necessary? Describe the tying process.*

9. *Tell how you would test the twine tension and set it properly.*

10. *What is trip tension and what effect does it have upon the bundles? How is trip tension tested and adjusted?*

11. *What has the twine holder spring to do with efficient tying?*

12. *How and why is the needle advanced?*

13. *Describe the knotter cam and knotter frame adjustments and the purpose of each.*

14. *Name some of the common tying troubles and tell how each is corrected.*

15. *What causes the tongue truck to tip and how may this be remedied?*

Chapter XII.

COMBINE HARVESTERS

The territory in which the combine harvester is used has spread from the wheatfields of the Pacific Coast states to the fields of practically every section of the country. Each year finds this cost-reducing, labor-saving machine proving its value to farmers in new regions. In recent years, the small combine, serving the individual farmer having comparatively small acreage, has made the harvesting of small grain and many seed crops a family affair.

The combine, in many cases, effects a saving of from fifteen to twenty cents per bushel in harvesting costs. It displaces the binder, hand shocking, pitching, and threshing. In one operation, the grain is cut and threshed, the cleaned grain elevated into a storage tank, and the straw scattered on the field to be plowed under for humus.

Figure 150—A small combine harvesting a fine crop of wheat.

Combines may be divided into three general types:

(1) The "straight-through" type. In combines of this design the grain is carried from the cutter bar straight back through the threshing cylinder and separating mechanism. A typical straight-through combine is illustrated in Figs. 150, 151, and 155. This smaller combine, commonly referred to as a one-man machine, derives power for its operation from the power take-off of the tractor;

(2) The "three-wheel-in-line" type. This construction is fairly restricted to the larger machines. A combine of this type is illustrated in Figs. 152, 153, and 156. It is powered by an integral power unit which operates cutting, threshing, separating, cleaning, and straw-spreading units;

(3) The self-propelled combine, Fig. 154, is especially adapted to the grain harvest on large acreages of the Great Plains and, with special equipment, for conditions as they exist in rice harvest. The self-propelled combine, as its name implies, provides its own motive or propelling power as well as power for cutting, threshing, separating, and cleaning

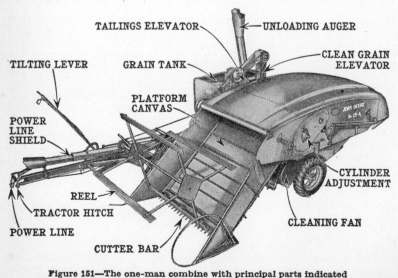

Figure 151—The one-man combine with principal parts indicated

the grain. The operator, seated high on the machine, has a clear, direct view of his work with all controls conveniently located for easy adaptability to changing field conditions. In fundamental design, it is of the "straight-through" type, the grain progressing in a straight line from cutter bar, through the rasp-bar cylinder, and separating mechanism.

The operator of the combine shown in Fig. 152, controls the machine from his position on the operator's platform. He has a clear view of the grain and stubble and is in position to watch the work his machine is doing. Fig. 153 illustrates the position of the operator in relation to his machine. One man is required to operate the tractor that pulls the combine and one or more men are needed to haul away the grain. When contrasting the size of this crew with the size of crew required to operate binders and a stationary threshing outfit, it is apparent that a great saving in labor costs can be made with a combine.

The demand for a small combine for the smaller and medium-sized farms where diversified farming is practiced,

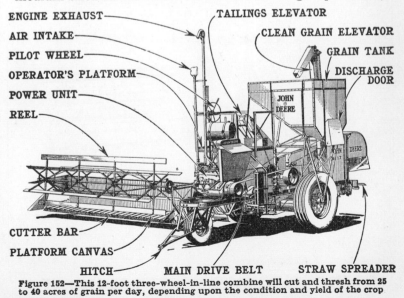

Figure 152—This 12-foot three-wheel-in-line combine will cut and thresh from 25 to 40 acres of grain per day, depending upon the condition and yield of the crop

has brought to the market the one-man combine which is so constructed that it can be used successfully in harvesting many different crops, including soybeans, in addition to all small grains and many seed crops. With this machine, the farmer with an average acreage of small grains can handle his harvest at lowest possible costs.

Principle of Operation. The combine performs four major operations—it cuts the grain, threshes or beats the kernels from the heads, separates the kernels from the straw, and cleans the grain, removing dirt and chaff before the grain is elevated into the storage tank.

The cutting unit operates much the same as a binder, with the exception that it is built to cut higher and to deliver the heads and straw into the threshing unit.

The threshing unit, which performs the threshing, separating, and cleaning operations, is similar in construction to

Figure 153—Overhead view of a combine, illustrating what the operator sees from his position on the control platform.

the stationary thresher. Cross-sectional views of two types of combines and a description of how the grain progresses through the machines will be found on pages 156-157 and 158-159. Careful study of these illustrations and the accompanying explanation will provide an understanding of the operating principles of the combine.

The larger combines have auxiliary motors which operate the mechanism, leaving the weight of the machine as

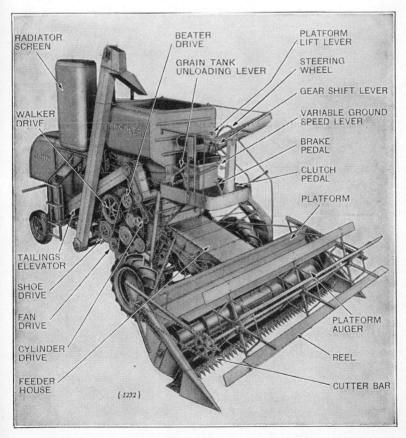

Figure 154—Some important units of the self-propelled combine are indicated in this view.

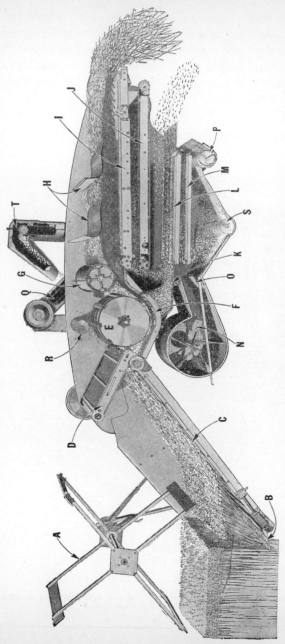

Figure 155—Cross-sectional view of straight-through combine showing how grain passes through the machine. See description below.

This cutaway view of the straight-through combine shows how the grain and straw are handled from the cutter bar straight through the machine.

The four-slat, ground-driven reel, "A", divides the grain and holds it to the cutter bar, "B". The cut grain is elevated by platform canvas, "C", which, together with feeder, "D", delivers grain in a thin, even stream to the rasp-bar cylinder, "E".

As the grain travels between cylinder, "E", and concave and perforated grate, "F", and back against beater, "G", behind cylinder, the greater part of separation takes place. The grain falls through perforated grate to shoe pan, "K", and is moved back to shoe chaffer, "L". Beater, "G", deflects grain down through the chaffer section at the front end of the straw rack, and passes the straw onto full-width straw rack, "I". During its outward movement, the remaining grain falls through cells in rack onto grain conveyor, "J", and is delivered back to shoe pan, "K", which moves it to front end of chaffer. Straw is then tossed out on the ground.

A blast of air from fan, "N", is directed by deflector, "O", against shoe chaffer, "L", and shoe sieve, "M". This blast, with the aid of chaffer and sieve agitation, blows chaff away and moves the tailings to tailings auger, "P". This auger carries them to tailings elevator, "Q", which conveys them to auger, "R", where they are delivered to the center of the cylinder for re-threshing.

Clean grain, after dropping through shoe chaffer, "L", and shoe sieve, "M", is carried by clean grain auger, "S", to elevator, "T", on opposite side of combine and elevated into grain tank.

Figure 156—Cross-sectional view of a three-wheel-in-line combine showing the important parts. Explanation of the progress of the grain through the machine appears below.

The units are lettered in this cross-sectional view so that the travel of the grain and straw can be followed.

The cut grain is carried by the platform canvas and elevator canvases to the feeder house cross conveyor, "A". This conveyor, with aid of feeder house beater, "B", feeds grain to cylinder, "C".

As the grain travels between cylinder, "C", and concaves, "D", over finger grates, "E", and back against the beater behind cylinder, "F", the greater part of separation takes place. Beater, "F", strips straw from cylinder and deflects grain and distributes straw evenly onto straw walkers, "G". Most of the grain and chaff fall through bottom of concaves, "D", and finger grates, "E", onto elevator, "K", below cylinder.

Straw and remaining loose grain are carried over to straw walkers, "G". Combined metal and canvas retarder, "H", assists beater in retarding straw in rapid movement and keeps grain from being thrown over. Straw is agitated by straw walkers, "G", on its outward movement, and remaining grain falls through opening in walkers and flows back to front of shoe through grain return pans, "I". Straw is then tossed out on spreader, "J".

After the grain and chaff leave elevator, "K", a blast of air from undershot fan, "N", through port, "O", is directed against chaffer, "L", and lower sieve, "M". This, with aid of sieve agitation, blows chaff away and moves tailings to tailings auger, "P". This auger carries them to tailings elevator, "Q", which conveys them to return opening, "S", and back into feeder house.

In tailings elevator, "Q", is sieve, "R", which lets any clean grain through into return spout which delivers it to carrier behind cylinder, preventing cracking of clean grain in going through threshing unit a second time.

Clean grain, after dropping through chaffer, "L", and sieve, "M", is carried by clean grain auger, "T", to elevator, "U", on opposite side of machine which delivers it to the grain tank, "V".

the only load for the tractor to pull. The smaller combines, as mentioned previously, are usually operated by the tractor engine through the power take-off—auxiliary motor can be furnished if desired as shown in Fig. 163.

Windrowing Method. In many conditions, it is desirable to cut the grain with a windrower and thresh it later with the regular combine equipped with pick-up attachment. When there are many weeds in the grain, when there is considerable moisture at harvest time, or when the crop ripens unevenly, this method of combine harvesting is used to advantage.

The windrower, shown in Fig. 159, consists of the usual cutting-unit platform, sickle, canvases, and reel. These parts are driven either by a power drive shaft from the tractor or through a ground drive. An opening at the inner end of the platform permits the cut grain to drop out on the stubble in windrow form.

Figure 157—Harvesting a fine crop of wheat with the self-propelled combine.

When the grain is properly cured or when the moisture content is sufficiently low, a special windrow pick-up platform is attached to the combine, or the pick-up unit is attached to the regular combine platform. Its function is to elevate the grain onto the combine platform and, from this point on, the threshing, separating, and cleaning processes are the same as described for the regular combine. Pick-up attachments are illustrated in Figs. 160 and 161.

The windrow method of combine harvesting has extended the boundaries within which the combine may be used. Many sections where weeds or rainfall have delayed the introduction of the combine are now using the windrow method with remarkable success.

Operation and Care.   All details of the operation, care, and repair of combines will not be given in this text because the actual servicing of combines will vary widely with the type and manufacturer's design. It is wise, therefore, to follow carefully the operating instructions furnished by manu-

Figure 158—Here the self-propelled combine is at work in conditions typical of the rice harvest.

facturers with the machines they sell. The operator should familiarize himself with these servicing and operating instructions so that he can operate his equipment with greatest efficiency.

Certain essentials to successful operations are stressed by all manufacturers, however, and some of these are mentioned here.

The maximum saving of grain and the quality of work done in all conditions depend very largely upon the operator's making best use of the adjustments provided for varying conditions. The grain in the tank, the tailings, the straw coming over the straw walkers or racks, and the material going over the shoe reveal the quality of work being done and indicate what adjustments are necessary.

The tractor operator should vary the travel speed to meet conditions. As he approaches a very heavy, down, or tangled condition, he should slow down to give the combine a chance to do a thorough, clean job of separating. In some conditions, it may be advisable to cut less than a full swath, giving the combine every opportunity to do good work. By listening constantly to the sound of the motor, the tractor operator can tell approximately how fast he should travel.

Figure 159—Windrower used for cutting and windrowing the grain which is later picked up with the pick-up attachment used on a regular combine, and threshed.

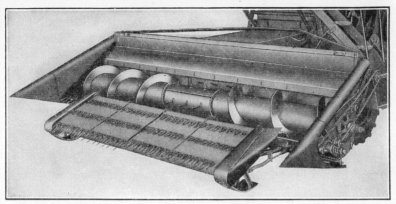

Figure 160—Pick-up attachment for combine attached to the short pick-up platform. The windrowed grain is elevated onto the platform which carries it into the combine in the regular way.

The combine operator should not only adjust his machine to hold threshing losses to a minimum, but he should also adjust and operate the platform and reel to reduce cutting losses. He should watch for stones and other foreign material that the platform may gather, and stop his machine before such obstructions reach the cylinder and cause damage.

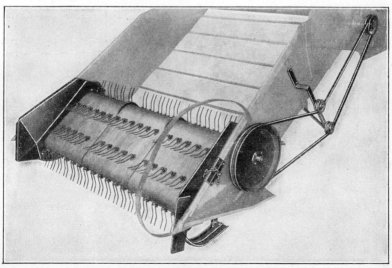

Figure 161—Pick-up attachment shown in place on a one-man straight-through combine.

Safety first should always be the rule when working around a combine. Never attempt to make repairs while the machine is running. Be careful when working around belts and chains. The great majority of accidents around combines result from carelessness.

Proper oiling is of first importance. The large number of bearings in a combine necessitate careful attention to regular and thorough oiling. The combines shown are provided with a high-pressure grease-gun oiling system which greatly facilitates proper lubrication.

The upkeep expense on a combine will be greatly reduced if all bolts are kept tight, and belts, canvases, and chains operated at correct tension. Regular inspection of the entire machine will save delays and reduce operating costs to a minimum.

At the end of each season it is important that all dust and chaff be cleaned from the inside and outside of the machine. If not removed, such material will gather moisture and cause

Figure 162—A hillside combine at work in the far western wheat territory.

steel parts to rust and wood to swell or rot. It will pay the owner of a combine to overhaul and clean the machine thoroughly at the close of each season.

Questions

1. *Name three types of combines used in your community.*

2. *Describe the principle of the combine.*

3. *What are its advantages over other methods of harvesting small grains?*

4. *What are some of the important points to remember in operating a combine? In storing it?*

5. *Describe the windrow method of combining and the machines used.*

6. *How may the tractor operator aid in doing a clean job of harvesting?*

7. *Why is "Safety First" a good motto for combine operators?*

Figure 163—An auxiliary engine furnishes power for operating the small combine shown here.

Chapter XIII.
CORN BINDERS

The corn binder is practically a necessity to the farmer who cuts his corn for ensilage, for fodder, or for shredding. With a corn binder, he can cut and bind from five to seven acres per day while his neighbor is cutting from one to one and one-half acres with a corn knife. The saving in time and labor that can be made with a corn binder pays for its cost in a short time.

Corn binders are built in horse-drawn ground-driven type (Fig. 164) and tractor-drawn power-driven type (Fig. 165). The former type has been used successfully for many years while the latter has been introduced since the advent of the tractor. The principal advantages of the tractor binder lie in the fact that it is power driven and does not depend upon

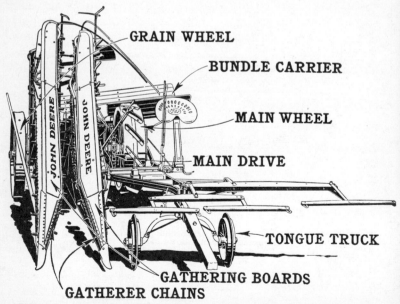

GRAIN WHEEL

BUNDLE CARRIER

MAIN WHEEL

MAIN DRIVE

TONGUE TRUCK

GATHERING BOARDS

GATHERER CHAINS

Figure 164—Corn binder with tongue truck and power-driven bundle carrier.

traction of a bull wheel for power. It will operate successfully in practically any field condition where a tractor will operate. It provides greater daily cutting capacity because of the faster, steadier travel of the tractor. Because of their similarity in construction, the operation and care of horse and tractor corn binders need not be discussed separately.

Like the grain binder, the corn binder gives the best service when it is given better than ordinary care and attention. It is not difficult to operate and adjust if the operator is familiar with the more common causes of trouble and knows how to correct them.

The corn binder is composed of three main units—the cutting, elevating, and binding units. Each has a definite and vital bearing upon the satisfactory operation of the binder. Each must be in perfect adjustment if the binder is to do its best work.

Cutting Unit Important. On the corn binder, the cutting parts are subjected to greater strain than any other part of the machine. This is due to the size of the stalks, their comparative hardness, and the fact that the load comes intermittently as the hills are reached. Even in the best of condi-

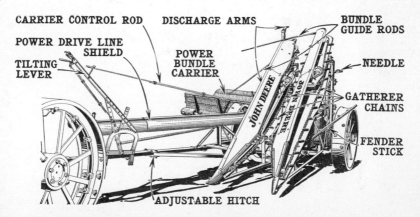

Figure 165—Tractor corn binder with important operating parts named.

tions, there is a much greater strain on the cutting unit of the corn binder than on the cutting parts of a grain binder.

To operate efficiently with the lightest draft under these severe conditions, the cutting parts of a corn binder must be sharp, properly aligned, and set to run smoothly. Fig. 166 shows the complete cutting unit in proper adjustment.

Two stationary knives, one on either side in front of the sickle, aid in cutting the stalks as they approach the sickle. These knives must be kept sharp and set to a shear cut with the sickle. They can be removed and sharpened with very little difficulty. When replaced, the bevel edges should be down. Because of the fact that the side knives and the sickle are often forced to work in the dirt, frequent sharpening of both is necessary. Dull cutting parts increase the draft, add to the strain on the driving mechanism, and may cause clogging of the machine.

The sickle must run freely, yet fit snugly in the guides provided. If the sickle head becomes worn, the knife head guide is adjusted to take up the wear by loosening the two nuts and adjusting the guide in the slotted holes. (See Fig. 166.) When this adjustment is properly made, the sickle and side knives make a shear cut—one of the big essentials to light draft and good work in a corn binder.

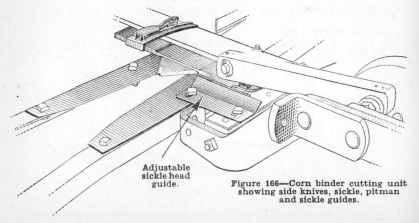

Adjustable
sickle head
guide.

Figure 166—Corn binder cutting unit
showing side knives, sickle, pitman
and sickle guides.

Elevating Unit. The elevating unit consists of six carrier chains, two chains on each of the upper gathering boards, and two chains on the lower part of the inner gatherer. The purpose of these chains is to elevate the corn in an upright posi-

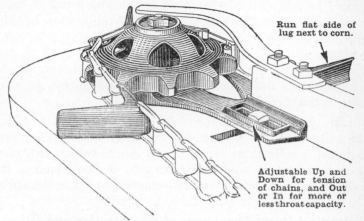

Run flat side of lug next to corn.

Adjustable Up and Down for tension of chains, and Out or In for more or less throat capacity.

Figure 167—Top chain tightener is adjustable two ways.

tion from the sickle to the binding unit. Their efficiency depends upon adjustment to the proper tension and position, which can best be determined by observation in the field.

Convenient tighteners are provided for each of the chains. They should be so adjusted that the chains run freely and are not too tight.

In addition to the adjustment for tightening the top chains, there is an adjustment provided for controlling the throat capacity or the distance between these chains. (See Fig. 167.) In cutting unusually tall corn on a windy day, it is often necessary to set the chains closer together to bring the tops back at the same speed as the butts. If it is desired to retard the tops, the throat capacity is increased by setting the chains farther apart. This is often necessary in cutting short corn.

Another aid to cutting short corn is provided in the small, round retarding spring. It may be set with the end tight against the binder deck. In this position, it holds the tops back, causing the corn to elevate in an upright position.

The lugs on the elevating chains serve as fingers that carry the stalks along. Chains that operate opposite to each other should be adjusted so that the lugs alternate rather than match as they move along the throat of the binder. In this adjustment, they are most efficient, and the danger of ears wedging between lugs and interfering with the work of elevating is eliminated. Note, in Fig. 167, the lugs in proper adjustment; the flat side of the lugs should always be run next to the corn, as shown.

Long steel springs are provided in the lower part of the throat to hold the corn against the lower chains. They are fastened to adjustable brackets and should be set with just enough tension to hold the stalks into the butt chains. In weedy conditions, more tension is applied to aid in elevating the extra quantity of material to be handled.

Binding Unit. The details of the operation and adjustment of the corn binder binding unit are practically the same as those given for the grain binder in a preceding chapter. Adjustments for tying troubles, twine tension, etc., are the same on both. A review of this text matter will furnish sufficient material for practical study of the corn binding unit.

Field Operation. The first field adjustment necessary is setting the binder to the height it is desired to cut the corn. In some cases, as in cutting corn infested with the European corn borer, it is desired to cut as close to the ground as possible, while in other cases, high cutting is more practical. Height is controlled by cranks on both the main and grain wheels. The binder works best when the wheels are set at the same height. If additional traction is needed, it can be secured by lowering the main wheel.

The grain wheel axle is constructed so that the weight of the binder can be shifted forward or backward to balance the machine properly with any equipment. (See Fig. 168.) The wheel is shifted to the rear to prevent whipping of the pole, or to place proper weight on the tongue truck. It is shifted forward to relieve neck weight when the tongue truck is not used.

The binder is tilted with the tilting lever to adjust the position of the gatherers with relation to the ground. This setting is governed by the condition of the corn to be cut. If the corn is down, the gatherer points should be run close to the ground.

The butt pan, upon which the butts slide from the sickle to the binding head, is adjusted up or down at the rear with the pan lever. The binder should be operated with the pan as low as possible, raising it only when it is necessary to place the band closer to the butts.

Bundle Carrier. The power bundle carrier is set into operation by tripping a foot lever. It delivers the bundles beyond the path of the horses as they make the next round. This eliminates the waste caused by the horses tramping the corn and does away with the hard work of dumping the bundles and returning the carrier, which is necessary when the old-fashioned bundle carrier is used. A safety clutch in the carrier drive removes the possibility of breakage should the forward motion of the carrier be checked for any reason. The spring tension on the clutch is adjustable to meet varying loads that may be carried.

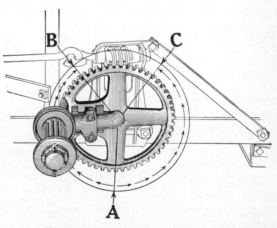

Figure 168—Grain wheel adjustment for balancing corn binder, showing grain wheel set to rear between points "A" and "B" to keep stiff pole from whipping, or to keep enough weight on tongue truck. Set wheel to front between "A" and "C" on binder with stiff pole, but without carrier.

Bundle Elevator. Some manufacturers of corn binders furnish bundle elevators as extra equipment for their machines. The purpose of this attachment is to elevate bundles direct from the binder, onto the wagon which is drawn beside the outfit. A tractor binder with bundle elevator is shown at work in Fig. 169, while a detail view of this equipment is illustrated in Fig. 170.

The bundle elevator is used principally for handling corn that is to be put into silos. The usual practice where this elevator is not used is to drop the bundles on the ground with the regular bundle carrier, then lift them onto the wagons by hand and haul to the ensilage cutter. Lifting tall, green bundles is hard, tiresome work; the bundle elevator does away with this job.

The bundles fall directly onto the elevating chain of the bundle elevator as they are discharged from the binding unit. They are elevated onto the wagon where one man can place them on the load. Handling bundles in this manner is easy compared with lifting them onto the wagon. And, too, the loose leaves and ears are elevated with the bundles—all the crop is delivered clean and dirt-free.

Figure 169—The bundle elevator on the corn binder is a great labor-saver. It elevates bundles, loose ears, and leaves directly onto the wagon.

Oiling Important. Frequent and thorough oiling of all bearings, chains, and working parts of the corn binder will reduce wear and add to its efficiency. The operator must be sure to keep the bearings of the binding unit oiled properly.

Figure 170—Overhead view of a tractor corn binder with bundle elevator and wagon hitch. For filling silos, this type of outfit cuts man-labor, saves time, and saves loose ears and leaves.

Before the binder is stored, it should be cleaned of all dirt and oil accumulations and inspected for worn parts. If new parts are needed, they should be ordered and attached during slack seasons, ready for the next year's work.

Questions

1. *What are the main advantages of a tractor corn binder over a horse-drawn binder?*
2. *Name the main units of a corn binder and tell the function of each.*
3. *Why is it important that cutting parts be kept sharp and in proper*

adjustment?

4. *Why are the elevating chains an important factor in good binding?*

5. *What adjustments are necessary in cutting short corn? In cutting tall corn on a windy day?*

6. *How is height of cutting controlled? How is the binder balanced?*

7. *What is the purpose of the tilting lever?*

8. *What are the advantages of a power bundle carrier?*

9. *Tell the more important points in properly caring for a corn binder.*

Chapter XIV.

ENSILAGE HARVESTERS

We have seen how the corn binder, especially when equipped with bundle elevator, materially reduced the amount of heavy work necessary in cutting corn for ensilage. However, with this equipment, the work of unloading heavy, green bundles and feeding them into the ensilage cutter still remains as a tedious part of putting up the crop.

Where row-crops are to be cut for ensilage, the field ensilage harvester solves the problem with the minimum of work, at extremely low cost, and enables the silo owner to harvest the crop at just the right time to make high-grade ensilage.

In principle, the field ensilage harvester embodies two separate units. The power-driven harvesting unit consists of the gathering and cutting parts, somewhat similar in design to corresponding parts used on the corn binder, in combination with a high-speed cutting unit designed to

Figure 171—From standing corn to top-grade ensilage in one operation.

cut the corn into lengths suitable for ensilage. A second unit, the blower, is stationed at the silo; its function is to blow the ensilage into the silo.

In operation, the cutting and gathering parts of the harvester unit cut the corn and deliver it to the feed rolls which pass it on to the cutting unit. Here, the revolving cutterhead, driven by the tractor engine through the power shaft, cuts the crop into suitable lengths, and passes the freshly-cut ensilage into the wagon through the curved delivery spout.

The blower unit, stationed at the silo, finishes the job by elevating the ensilage into the silo.

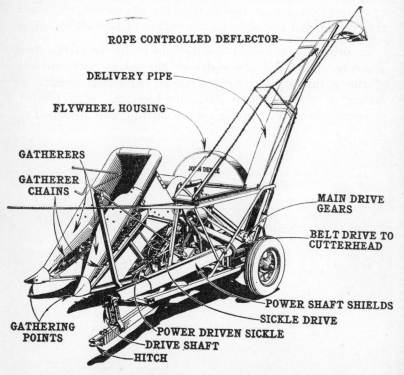

ROPE CONTROLLED DEFLECTOR

DELIVERY PIPE

FLYWHEEL HOUSING

GATHERERS

GATHERER CHAINS

MAIN DRIVE GEARS

BELT DRIVE TO CUTTERHEAD

POWER SHAFT SHIELDS

SICKLE DRIVE

GATHERING POINTS

POWER DRIVEN SICKLE

DRIVE SHAFT

HITCH

Figure 172—The harvesting unit of the ensilage harvester with important parts indicated.

The details of operating and adjusting the feeding, cutting, and elevating parts of the field harvester are so similar to those given in a following chapter for comparable parts of the field hay chopper, that a further discussion of them is not necessary. Most important in caring for the cutting unit, which runs at high speed, is providing sufficient lubrication to all parts and keeping all bearings tight and knives in good repair. Servicing the knives and shear plate of the ensilage harvester shown follows the procedure given for the field hay chopper.

The blower, like the cutting unit of the harvester, should be kept thoroughly lubricated to insure efficient operation

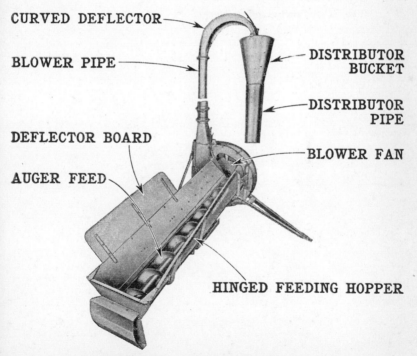

CURVED DEFLECTOR

BLOWER PIPE

DISTRIBUTOR BUCKET

DISTRIBUTOR PIPE

DEFLECTOR BOARD

AUGER FEED

BLOWER FAN

HINGED FEEDING HOPPER

Figure 173—The blower unit is stationed at the silo to handle the ensilage from wagon to silo.

and long life. As is the case with all high-speed equipment, especial attention should be given to proper adjustment and lubrication of all parts, and to keeping all nuts tight.

When the season's work is done, both units should be cleaned thoroughly and inspected for worn parts which should be replaced with new parts during the slack season.

Questions

1. *What are the advantages of using the field ensilage harvester?*
2. *Describe the main parts of the harvester unit and mention their purpose.*
3. *How is the cutting unit driven?*
4. *How are knives sharpened and adjusted?*
5. *What is the function of the blower?*

Chapter XV.

CORN PICKERS

Wherever corn is husked, either for the market or for feeding purposes, the corn picker is more generally used each year. The hard work of husking by hand is fast being replaced by the easier, faster, and less expensive mechanical method.

The corn picker has been refined and simplified, mechanically, to a point where its operation is not difficult. With the aid of the manufacturer's operator's manual, furnished with each new machine, the average farmer finds the corn picker comparatively easy to operate.

When mechanical corn pickers were first introduced, the one-row, horse-drawn, ground-driven type was the only type manufactured. With the advent of tractors and power farming came the power-driven one-row and, later, the power-driven two-row pickers (Fig. 178), which have greatly increased the corn-picking capacity of one man. With a power-

Figure 174—The mechanical picker reduces cost of harvesting corn.

driven picker, equipped with wagon hitch, one man has control of tractor, picker, and wagon.

The push-type or mounted-type picker, such as illustrated in Fig. 174, which, when attached to the tractor makes up a compact, easily-handled one-man picking outfit, was a natural development following the advent of the general-purpose tractor and the general trend to integral or tractor-mounted equipment. Its advantages lie in the fact that no hand-picking is necessary in opening fields, that the corn is handled in a direct line from the snapping rolls to the wagon elevator, and in the fact that, with gatherers in front of the tractor, the operator has a good view of the work at all times. With its rear delivery, a direct center hitch is provided for the wagon, thereby eliminating side draft. In addition, the mounted picker is easily transported from field to field, since its control is just as easy as driving the tractor.

Comparatively new in picker design is the wheel-and-drawbar mounted type (Figs. 176 and 177), especially adapted

Figure 175—The power-driven two-row picker speeds up the work of harvesting.

to the smaller tractors. In this type of picker, weight is distributed between tractor drawbar and wheel of the picker. Its advantages lie in its simplicity and ease of attaching and detaching.

How They Work. The function of corn pickers is to snap the ears from stalks, remove husks and silks, and deliver the cleaned ears into a wagon. To do this, three main units are required—the snapping, husking, and elevating units. Efficiency of the picker depends to a great extent upon the correct adjustment of the snapping and husking units.

Figure 176—The-wheel-and-drawbar mounted picker at work in the field.

Power to operate the corn picker is furnished direct from the tractor engine through a power drive shaft. Thus, the tractor engine, running at steady speed insures uniform power for operating snapping, husking, and elevating units.

The principle of operation of one-row and two-row pickers is so similar that both will be covered in the following text.

Snapping Unit. As the cornstalks advance between the gatherers, they are drawn into the snapping rolls with the aid of gathering chains, one on the inner and two on the outer gatherers. The stalks pass between the rolls while the ears are snapped off and carried to the husking unit. Snapping rolls are illustrated in Fig. 179.

The snapping rolls are adjusted according to the condition of the corn; if damp, rolls are run close together, but not touching; if dry, the rolls are set to run farther apart. They should never be run closer together than necessary for good work—to do so increases the draft. The desired setting is secured by an adjustment provided.

A tension spring at the upper end of the rolls permits obstructions to pass between the rolls without breakage of parts. It should be set with just enough tension to keep the gears well in mesh. Too much tension may cause breakage.

Figure 177—Front quarter view of wheel-and-drawbar mounted one-row picker, showing picker carrying wheel.

Husking Rolls. The husking rolls operate in pairs. They are held together under spring pressure at either end and are adjusted by tightening or loosening two nuts. There should be just enough tension on the rolls to cause them to grasp the husks when the smooth surfaces come together. Too much tension will increase the draft unnecessarily.

Movement of the ears over the rolls of the machines illustrated in this chapter, is controlled to assure clean husking.

Wagon Elevator. The elevating unit carries the husked ears from the elevator hopper into the wagon.

Figure 178—Overhead view of a two-row corn picker with tractor and wagon attached. The lines indicate the position of the rows in relation to picker, tractor, and wagon.

The hopper, into which the ears fall after the husking process is finished, is large enough to hold the surplus corn delivered to it when the elevator is stopped to change wagons and when turning.

The elevator drive is provided with a safety clutch (Fig. 180) which prevents breakage of chains and other parts if the elevator becomes clogged. The same type of clutch is also provided on the gatherers, first elevator, husking rolls, and husk conveyor for the same purpose. The springs controlling these clutches should have just enough tension to hold the clutch in contact when the parts are working under normal load. If clogging occurs, and the added load throws the clutch out, the operator should stop immediately, locate and correct the trouble.

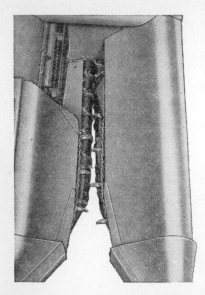

Figure 179—Above is shown a detailed drawing of the snapping unit and first elevator of a one-row picker. The galvanized top has been removed from the gatherer to show the working parts.

Oiling Important. The corn pickers shown are provided with roller and ball bearings at the important wearing points, all of which are supplied with facilities that make oiling easy.

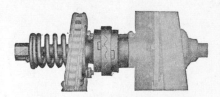

Figure 180—Slip clutches protect the main working parts of the corn picker against breakage should congestion occur.

All chains should be brushed with a light oil occasionally and should be run just tight enough to prevent jumping.

Questions

1. *Describe three types of corn pickers and outline their differences.*
2. *Name the advantages of a corn picker over the hand-picking method.*
3. *Describe the operation of a corn picker.*
4. *What are the three main units of a picker, and what is their purpose?*
5. *Why are safety clutches used and how do they operate?*
6. *Tell the important points in caring for a corn picker.*

Chapter XVI.
HAMMER AND ROUGHAGE MILLS

The hammer mill and the roughage mill have solved the feed-grinding problem on many farms, enabling the individual farmer to grind feed as the need arises and convenience permits, rather than to depend upon the custom grinder for this important work.

The modern hammer mill is designed to grind practically every type of feed, including small grain, shelled or ear corn, fodder, and hay, to the size best adapted to the feeding purpose for which it is intended. With the wide variety of screens available for present-day mills, feeds may be ground to any practical degree of fineness ranging from extremely fine meal or flour to coarse roughage.

Many of the present mills may be operated successfully by electric motors of 3- to 10-H.P. using the motor mounting attachment supplied by the manufacturer. Where electric power is available, the electric motor drive is used to power the mill while the farm tractor is free for other jobs.

Two units make up the hammer mill, as shown in Fig. 182. The material to be ground is fed into the chamber of

Figure 181—The small hammer mill is shown here powered by an electric motor

the mill where the hammers, revolving at high speed, cut it in mid-air, throw it against the breaker bars to be picked up and recut until it is reduced to particles small enough to pass through the screen which determines the fineness of the grinding. As the ground material passes through the screen, a suction fan draws it from the mill and forces it through the blowpipe into the feed collector for final delivery to sacks, bins, or wagons.

The first step in preparing the hammer mill for operation is to select the proper screen, place it in the screen groove, and lock it in position, making certain that the screen and screen lock are seated properly. The air suction control should be set so that the proper amount of air is drawn through the screen for efficient grinding. When grinding on an extremely fine screen, more air should be drawn through the screen so that light hulls which, with a lighter suction, would rotate with the rotor will be reduced quickly

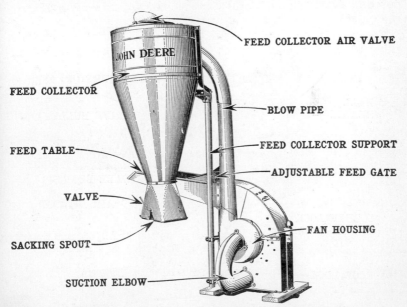

Figure 182—The hammer mill complete with feed collector.

and drawn through the screen. When extremely coarse screens are used, the suction slide may be closed entirely. A two-piece feed control on the feed table governs the flow of material from the feed table to the mill: the smaller gate is used when feeding small grains (including shelled corn) while, for ear corn, both gates are raised just high enough to permit the ears to pass. Except when grinding hay or fodder, feed control should always be in place to regulate the air intake at the feed opening.

In adjustment, the hammer mill is free of complicated problems. There are, however, several basic facts which the operator must keep in mind constantly. In the first place, the rotor shaft of the hammer mill turns at high speed; therefore, special attention should be given to proper greas-

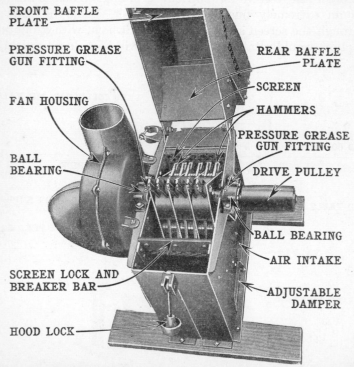

FRONT BAFFLE
PLATE

PRESSURE GREASE
GUN FITTING

FAN HOUSING

BALL
BEARING

SCREEN LOCK AND
BREAKER BAR

HOOD LOCK

REAR BAFFLE
PLATE

SCREEN

HAMMERS

PRESSURE GREASE
GUN FITTING

DRIVE PULLEY

BALL BEARING

AIR INTAKE

ADJUSTABLE
DAMPER

Figure 183—Detailed inside view of hammer mill showing rotor with hammers.

ing and proper adjustment of all bearings. The rotor shaft, with the hammer mounting plates, hammers, and spacing collars, must be kept in proper balance to insure freedom from vibration which would damage the bearings and shorten the life of the entire mill. To preserve this balance, all hammers must be sharpened, reversed, or replaced at the same time; in reassembling, particular care must be used to make certain that all cast-iron spacing collars are replaced in their original order. If vibration appears, the mill should be stopped immediately and checked carefully for broken hammers. When replacing a broken hammer, it is well to replace the corresponding hammers in the other banks to insure proper balance, as any small difference in weight will result in vibration.

When hammers are dulled from wear, they may be reversed to present new cutting steps. When both edges are dulled, hammers may be removed and sharpened on a good emery wheel. This is an important servicing operation, for

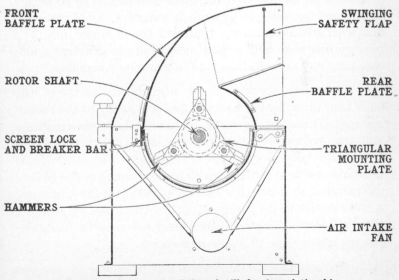

Figure 184—Cross-sectional view of mill showing relationship of operating parts.

the hammers must retain their original cutting steps for effective work. To insure best service from the hammer mill, hammers should be ground before they become too badly worn.

The blower and feed collector require but little attention other than an occasional inspection to be sure all joints are tight. An air control damper is provided so that the blast of air can be controlled to eliminate loss of light or exceptionally fine material. Thus, the operator may adjust the air pressure to insure proper movement of the ground material without forcing finely-ground meal through the sack.

Highly important in the successful operation of any hammer mill is the maintenance of rated speed as specified by the manufacturer of the mill.

The roughage mill (Fig. 185) may be considered a combination hammer mill and cutterhead mill since it incorporates the principles of the hammer mill for a final grinding, with a cutterhead for the first or rough grinding. The roughage mill, therefore, will handle a much wider variety of material, and with greater capacity, than will the hammer mill. The modern roughage mill is used successfully in grinding grain, chopping hay and ensilage, and in grinding roughages.

In operation, servicing, and adjustment, many of the basic facts given for the hammer mill will apply to the roughage mill. There are, however, certain parts of the roughage mill that require separate explanation. The knives of the three-blade lawn mower type cutterhead cut against a four-sided, reversible shear bar, making a first rough cut to reduce the material to a size that can be handled by the hammers. Knives should be kept in good cutting condition by grinding when necessary. The reversible shear bar may be turned to present a new edge to insure a clean cut.

Careful attention to lubrication and to proper adjustment of all moving parts will result in efficient operation and long life of the mill. Where the mill is used in the open, it should be covered when not in use to prevent damage by exposure to rain and snow. A periodic cleaning and inspection will repay the operator in smoother, more efficient operation.

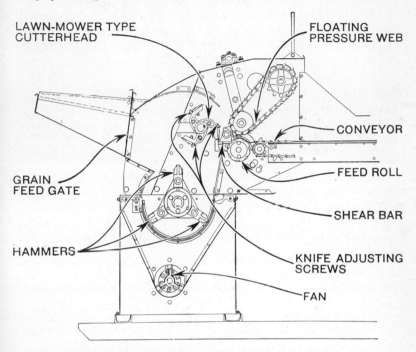

Figure 185—The roughage mill, showing location of parts.

Figure 186—Grinding forage with the roughage mill.

Questions

1. What is the most important point in the efficient operation of the hammer mill?

2. If your hammer mill developed excessive vibration, where would you look for trouble? How would you correct it?

3. How would you replace a complete set of hammers? A broken hammer? How would you sharpen the hammers?

4. What is the double purpose of the fan?

5. What is the purpose of the feed control?

6. What causes finely-ground feed to sift through the sack? How would you remedy this condition?

7. How would you regulate the air control for extremely coarse grinding? Extremely fine?

8. Describe the work of the roughage mill.

9. How does it differ from the hammer mill? How is it similar?

Chapter XVII.
POTATO DIGGERS

Modern potato diggers have taken much of the drudgery out of the potato harvest. They have reduced the waste common to the use of ordinary plows or hand-digging methods. A digger is practically a necessity to the economical production of potatoes for the markets.

There are two types of diggers in common use, the horse-drawn elevator type, and the tractor-drawn, tractor-powered elevator type, which is built in two styles: the angle bed as shown in Fig. 188, and the level bed as shown in Figs. 187 and 189. A further variation of the level bed digger is the double level bed digger especially adapted for light soil and extremely trashy conditions. On this digger, a single shovel spans two rows, to pass surface trash, soil and potatoes onto the double elevators. Since the level bed digger is growing in popularity due to its gentler handling of the crop, a digger of this style is being used for illustration here. These types are furnished with various equipment units which adapt them to practically all harvesting conditions.

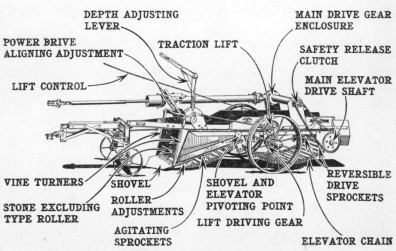

Figure 187—Level bed potato digger with important parts named.

Principle of Operation. The wide steel shovel, set to run at a safe depth below the potatoes, raises the potatoes, dirt, vines and all, onto the elevator. Depth is regulated by adjusting the lifting lever and beams.

Figure 188—Two-row tractor-drive angle bed digger.

The main object of the potato digger is to deliver clean potatoes on top of the soil. As stated above, the shovel, digging under the potatoes, loosens the soil and by the forward motion of the digger, the soil, potatoes, and vines are carried onto the elevator. The elevator is a continuous chain moving toward the rear of the machine. The earth drops through the elevator, aided by the agitating or up-and-down movement of the elevator. This agitation can be increased or decreased according to soil conditions by interchanging the smooth rollers and oblong agitating sprockets provided.

A shielded drive shaft, protected by a slip clutch, is used

Figure 189—Two-row level bed digger at work.

to transmit power direct from the tractor engine to operate elevators and separating mechanism.

The tractor-drive digger is especially advantageous under difficult conditions, as the speed of its power-driven elevator is not affected by wheel slippage or by sudden slowing of forward travel. Power for operating the elevator of the horse-drawn digger is furnished by traction of the wheels.

The modern potato digger is provided with a wide variety of adjustments to meet practically all conditions encountered in the field. Special equipment units are available for many diggers to adapt them to unusual harvesting requirements. For these reasons, it is well for the operator to make a careful study of the manufacturer's instruction booklet to familiarize himself with his machine and thereby be prepared to take full advantage of its capabilities.

Since the potato digger must work effectively in dusty and gritty conditions, lifting tons of earth, trash, and potatoes, especial attention should be given to thorough lubrication. Periodic check for badly-worn or broken parts and replacement where necessary, will repay the operator in better service in the field.

Questions

1. *Name two types of potato diggers and tell the advantages of each.*
2. *Which type is most popular in your community?*
3. *Describe the action of an elevator digger.*

Chapter XVIII.

MOWERS

Mowers are in use in all sections of the country, and their operation, care, and repair should be a matter of general knowledge among farmers. Heavy draft, ragged cutting, and excessive breakage can often be avoided by using the maximum of care in the oiling, adjusting, and replacing of parts. A smooth-running, clean-cutting mower gives real satisfaction to the operator and requires less power from horses or tractor. Fig. 190 shows a popular style of enclosed-gear mower with all main parts named.

The cutter bar and its parts, including the pitman shaft, (see Figs. 191 and 192) make up the most vital unit in mower operation. These parts do all the work of cutting; draft, repair costs, and length of life of the mower depend upon the proper setting and care given them.

Register of the Knife. The knife is the heart of the mower. Its sections must be sharp and firmly riveted to the knife back; the guards, wearing plates, and knife holders must

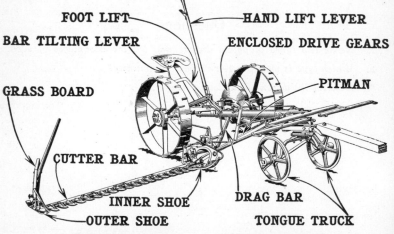

FOOT LIFT

BAR TILTING LEVER

HAND LIFT LEVER

ENCLOSED DRIVE GEARS

GRASS BOARD

PITMAN

CUTTER BAR

INNER SHOE

DRAG BAR

OUTER SHOE

TONGUE TRUCK

Figure 190—A popular type of enclosed-gear mower.

fit to it perfectly, holding it to a shear cut with the guard plates, if its work is to be efficient. Knife head guides must be properly set and bolted tight.

Register of the knife refers to the position of its sections in relation to the guards when the knife is at the outer end of its stroke and at the inner end of its stroke. The sections should be in the center of the guards when at the extremes of the strokes. Fig. 192 shows the knife in register on the inner end of the stroke.

If the knife does not register on its outward stroke, that is, if the sections do not reach center of guards, part of the vegetation is not cut. The results are an uneven job of cutting, an uneven load on the entire mower, heavier draft, and often, clogging of the mower knife. An incomplete inward stroke will result in the same troubles.

To test and correct the register of a mower knife, raise the tongue to working position—32 inches from underside of front end of tongue to the ground —and turn the flywheel over until knife is at outer end of stroke. It is necessary

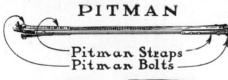

PITMAN

Pitman Straps
Pitman Bolts

WEARING PLATE

INNER SHOE

Figure 191—Details of mower cutter bar parts.

KNIFE

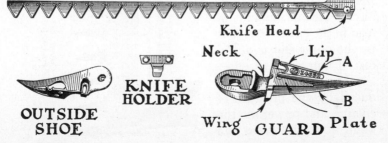

Knife Head

Neck   Lip
                      A

KNIFE HOLDER

OUTSIDE SHOE

Wing   GUARD   Plate
                      B

that pitman straps at both ends of pitman are tightened properly before making the test. If the sections do not center, an adjustment should be made. On most makes of mowers, register is obtained by adjusting the brace bar at the flywheel bowl. One complete turn of the brace bar will make 1/8-inch difference in register. In addition to this adjustment, forked washers are provided at both ends of the drag bar bearing on the mower shown in Fig. 190, so that knife will be properly centered without destroying the correct lead in the cutter bar. By transferring more or fewer washers from one end of the yoke to the other as may be necessary, and at the same time adjusting the brace bar, proper setting is obtained.

Cutter Bar Alignment. All new mowers have a certain amount of lead in the cutter bar; that is, the outer end is ahead of the inner end to offset the backward strain produced by the pressure of cutting and to permit the knife and pitman to run

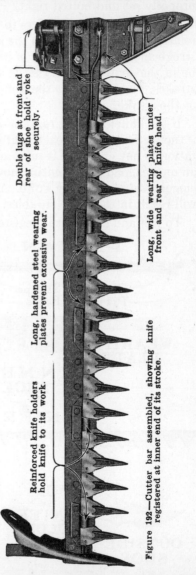

Double lugs at front and rear of shoe hold yoke securely.

Long, wide wearing plates under front and rear of knife head.

Long, hardened steel wearing plates prevent excessive wear.

Reinforced knife holders hold knife to its work.

Figure 192—Cutter bar assembled, showing knife registered at inner end of its stroke.

in a straight line. As the mower wears and parts become loose, the outer end of the bar lags back until the knife is running on a backward angle, causing undue wear and breakage of cutting parts. The outer end of the cutter bar should be ahead of the inner end 1 to 1-1/4 inches on 4-1/2-foot mowers; 1-1/4 to 1-1/2 inches on 5-foot mowers; 1-1/2 to 1-3/4 inches on 6-foot mowers; and 1-3/4 to 2 inches on 7-foot mowers.

To determine the lead or lack of lead in a cutter bar, raise the end of the tongue (underside) 32 inches from the ground. Then tie a cord to the oil cap on the pitman box ("A" in Fig. 193). Stretch the cord over the center of the knife head, as shown at "B", Fig. 193; the amount of lead in the bar can be determined at point "C". The upper illustration in Fig. 193 shows a 5-foot bar with the proper lead—approximately 1-1/4 inches.

The lower illustration in Fig. 193 shows a bar with nearly 4 inches of lag—a condition that would result in heavy draft and poor work were it not corrected. With the cord tied to the oil cap on the pitman box, "D", and stretched over the center of knife head at "E", the position of the outer

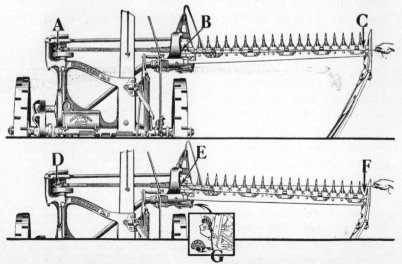

Figure 193—Overhead view of a mower showing how to determine lead or lag in the cutter bar.

end of the bar at "F" is seen to be 3 inches behind the straight line or approximately 4-1/4 inches behind the position at which it should be maintained for the correct amount of lead.

Lag in the cutter bar of the mower shown in Fig. 190 is removed and the bar brought up to

Figure 194—Eccentric "A" is adjusted to left to take up lag in cutter bar.

proper position by turning an eccentric bushing ("A" in Fig. 194) to the left until proper alignment is obtained.

After hard usage, enough wear may occur to create excessive free motion of cutter bar. In such cases, new parts may be necessary for effective adjustment.

Pitman Adjustment. The mower operator must keep the bolts that connect the pitman to the pitman box and knife head at proper tension for good work. If pitman bolts are too tight, particularly the knife head bolt, the draft will be increased. The knife head must have a free ball-and-socket action in the pitman straps (see Fig. 191) to accommodate tilting of the bar and the up-and-down movement of the inner and outer ends of the bar in going over uneven ground. If

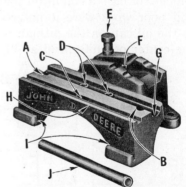

Figure 195—A convenient block for removing and replacing guard plates, knife sections, flywheel wrist pins, and for straightening knives. "A" and "B" are holes used in riveting wrist pin to flywheel. "C" indicates a hole through which sheared rivets are driven. Removable, hardened riveting posts are shown at "D". "E" is the guard plate riveting post. "F" indicates hole through which old rivet is driven. "G" is a groove for the knife back. When shearing sections, the knife back rests on edge "H". The grooves, "I", steady the knife. "J" is the rivet set used in completing the job of riveting.

the bar is tilted low, a tight pitman connection tends to hold the knife sections away from guard plates. This causes excessive wear and allows the grass to get between sections and guard plates.

If the pitman bolts are permitted to become too loose, or the strap rivets loosen, the pitman and knife are sub-

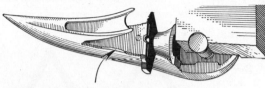

jected to excessive vibration, which results in heating of pitman box, breakage of parts, and abnormal wear.

Figure 196—The efficiency of the mower is seriously impaired by imperfect guard plates.

Operating the pitman with the hand will usually show whether or not it is in proper adjustment.

Adjustment and Repair of Cutter Bar Parts. (See Figs. 191 and 192.) When the pitman is properly adjusted and all cutter bar parts are set as they should be, the front end of every knife section rests smoothly on the guard plate, in position to make a shear cut. To maintain this ideal condition, guards and guard plates, wearing plates, and knife

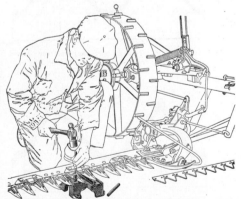

holders must be in good condition and correctly set. If these parts become loose or badly worn, the knife will flop around in the cutter bar, chewing and tearing the grass instead of cutting it, causing the mower to pull hard and increasing the possibilities of breakage.

Figure 197—Replacing guard plates in the field with the repair anvil, shown in Figure 195.

The guard or ledger plates have a very important function in the cutting action of the mower. They act as one-half of the shear, the knife sections acting as the other half. If sections and plates are not sharp or do not fit closely together, the result is similar to that produced by a dull or loose shears in cutting cloth. Guard plates should be replaced when broken or worn dull (Fig. 196) and the guards aligned to give a shear cut on every plate. Figs. 195 and 197 show a convenient block for replacing plates with guards either on or off the cutter bar.

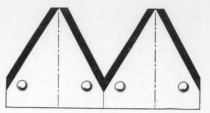

New sections—proper bevel and angle for good work.

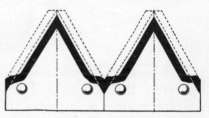

Sections properly ground. Even after repeated grinding, proper bevel and angle are retained.

A dull or improperly-ground knife reduces the efficiency of the mower, results in ragged cutting, excessive and unnatural wear, and extremely heavy draft. By actual dynamometer tests, a dull or improperly-ground knife may increase draft of the mower as much as 30 per cent over the normal draft of a new or properly-ground knife.

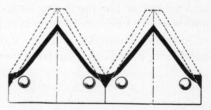

Improperly ground sections; narrow bevel and wrong angle which changes the angle of "shear."

The angle at which the sections work with the guard plates and the angle of the cutting bevel on new sections have been worked out by years of

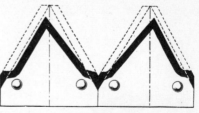

Sections ground off center, destroying the register of blade in guard.

Figure 198—The right and wrong ways to grind mower knives. Dotted lines show outline of new sections.

trial and experience; they are practically standard on all mowers. When grinding the knife, it is of utmost importance that these angles be retained if the knife is to be restored to its full efficiency. The angle at which the section meets the guard plate must be such that the grass will not have a tendency to slip away. The bevel of the section is highly important, as an abrupt edge will tend to dull easily and chew the grass, thereby increasing draft; too wide a bevel will cause the section to nick easily. (See Fig. 198.) Before grinding sections which have been reground previously, it is well to decide whether or not further grinding will be justified. As shown in Fig. 201, knife sections are extremely hard along the cutting edge and somewhat softer, to provide toughness and shock resistance, in the center. A knife section ground beyond the hardened outer area will not only fail to hold its cutting edge but, in most cases, will be too small for efficient service.

Bearing in mind the importance of retaining proper bevel and angle when sections are sharpened, it is well to select a knife grinder that can be set to restore the sections to original specifications.

When knife sections have been ground to the point where the efficiency of the mower is impaired (Fig. 201) or when sections have been broken, the worn or broken plates should be sheared off, as shown in Fig. 199. With knife back resting solidly on the block, strike back edge of section a sharp blow.

Figure 199—When removing and replacing knife sections, a solid base must be provided to prevent bending or breaking knife back.

This operation will shear the rivets without damaging knife back. Driving out the rivets with a punch not only enlarges the holes, but weakens the knife back.

In replacing the sections, be sure the rivets are *tight* and properly rounded.

Aligning the guards is an important and exacting operation. A new knife, or a straight one that is not badly worn, should be used in testing and setting the guards. Insert the knife and set each guard up or down, as necessary, to make a shear cut between knife section and guard plate. Guards are malleable iron and can be bent without breaking by striking at the thick part, just ahead of plate when guard bolt is tight. Guard wings should also be aligned, making a smooth surface for knife back to work against. Position of guard points should not be considered—the plates and wings are

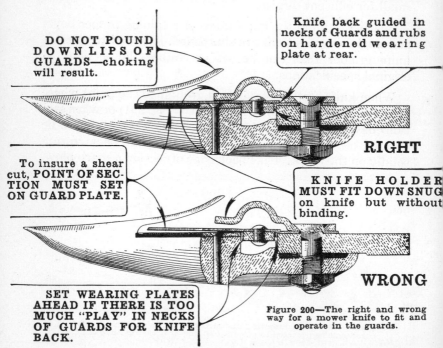

DO NOT POUND DOWN LIPS OF GUARDS—choking will result.

Knife back guided in necks of Guards and rubs on hardened wearing plate at rear.

RIGHT

To insure a shear cut, POINT OF SECTION MUST SET ON GUARD PLATE.

KNIFE HOLDER MUST FIT DOWN SNUG on knife but without binding.

WRONG

SET WEARING PLATES AHEAD IF THERE IS TOO MUCH "PLAY" IN NECKS OF GUARDS FOR KNIFE BACK.

Figure 200—The right and wrong way for a mower knife to fit and operate in the guards.

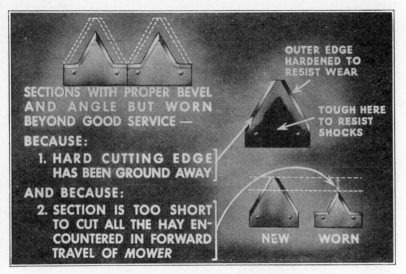

SECTIONS WITH PROPER BEVEL AND ANGLE BUT WORN BEYOND GOOD SERVICE —

BECAUSE:

1. HARD CUTTING EDGE HAS BEEN GROUND AWAY

AND BECAUSE:

2. SECTION IS TOO SHORT TO CUT ALL THE HAY ENCOUNTERED IN FORWARD TRAVEL OF MOWER

OUTER EDGE HARDENED TO RESIST WEAR

TOUGH HERE TO RESIST SHOCKS

NEW   WORN

Figure 201—Knife sections ground beyond good service.

the important units that must be aligned. See Fig. 200 for complete information on proper alignment of guards to produce a shear cut.

It is advisable to replace badly worn wearing plates (see Fig. 191, 196, and 200) when guards are repaired. The wearing plates hold the sections in correct cutting position, but when worn, they permit the sections to rise at front end, causing clogging and ragged cutting.

The knife holders hold the sections down against the guard plates. They must be set close enough to the sections to hold them firmly in position when cutting, yet not tight enough to cause binding and heavy draft.

When necessary to set the holders down, the knife should be pulled out—holders should never be set down with knife under them. Starting at holder next to the outer shoe, set each holder down with a hammer, tapping it lightly. Then move the knife under holder to test the adjustment; if it tends to bind, leave knife under the holder and hit the holder on the flat surface between the two bolts. Proper setting of each holder must be made before moving to the next one.

Lifting Spring. There should be enough tension on the lifting spring to cause the bar to rise easily and move steadily over the ground. With too much tension, the bar will not follow uneven ground, and the inner end may be held up after it has passed over a mound or other obstruction. When properly adjusted, the lifting spring carries the bulk of weight of the cutter bar on the wheels, increasing the traction and reducing friction between bar and the ground.

Clutch Adjustment. When clutch parts become worn, it is often necessary to make minor adjustments for good work. The clutch shifter rod is adjustable to take up wear and keep the clutch engaged full depth in drive gear. If the

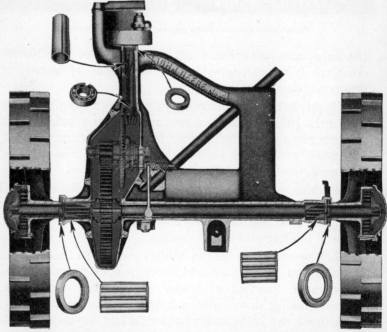

Figure 202—Cross-sectional view showing oiling system, gears, clutch, and bearings of the mower shown in Fig. 190. Color indicates parts that are oiled automatically.

mower does not go out or stay out of gear when shifter lever is moved down, it is evident the clutch shifter rod adjustment must be shortened. This is done by loosening the lock bolt on the clutch pedal and turning the clutch throw-out sleeve to the left. After proper adjustment is made, tighten lock bolt and secure with cotter key.

When the clutch lever is up and the clutch meshes full depth with gear, the clutch shifter yoke should be free in the clutch and not bind against either side of the groove in the clutch.

Operation and Care. Mowers require a considerable amount of attention and care when at work. Following are a few hints for mower operators:

See that all moving parts work freely before putting the machine in the field. Keep all nuts tight.

Use plenty of good grade oil, and never let wearing surfaces become dry.

Figure 203—A time-saving hook-up of power mower with tractor-drawn mower cutting from 50 to 70 acres per day.

Oiling of the mower shown in Fig. 190 is greatly simplified because all gears are enclosed and running in oil. In addition, the axle, wheel, gear, countershaft, and pitman shaft bearings are oiled automatically from the gear case, as shown in Fig. 202.

In dry, dusty, or sandy conditions, the cutting parts usually work best without oil.

The mower is in correct working position when underside of the tongue at the front end is 32 inches from the ground.

It is advisable to keep the horses close together by shortening the inside lines.

In summary, it can be said that the repairing of mower cutter bars is generally put off too long and that greater care in oiling and adjusting the important wearing parts will add to the length of the mower's life.

Questions

1. What is meant by register of a mower knife? What effect does lack of register have upon the work of a mower?

2. Tell how you would register a mower knife found to be out of register.

3. What is meant by "cutter bar" alignment? How would you test for alignment and how would you take up "lag", if present?

4. Why is it necessary to keep the pitman straps in proper adjustment?

5. Name the important parts of the cutter bar.

6. What is a "shear cut"? What parts must be in proper adjustment for this ideal cutting condition?

7. Describe proper procedure for grinding mower knives.

8. How are the guards aligned?

9. What is the function of the knife holders?

10. How would you set the lifting spring for good work?

11. What are the most important points in properly caring for a mower?

Tractor Mowers

Because of the fact that the general-purpose type of tractor must do all farm jobs if it is to displace horses on the farm, most manufacturers provide power-driven mowers that are quickly attached to and detached from the tractor. Greater mowing capacity is possible with a power-driven machine.

Operation. It is little more difficult to operate a tractor mower than it is to operate a horse-drawn mower. The cutting parts are practically the same in construction, and require the same care and adjustments for maximum efficiency.

Power for operating the mower shown in Fig. 204, is transmitted from the power take-off of the tractor to the pitman through a drive shaft and enclosed roller chain drive. A slip clutch in the power line releases automatically when the sickle clogs or when the strain of cutting in tough material is too great. Breakage of parts due to overstrains is practically eliminated if the operator keeps the tension on the slip

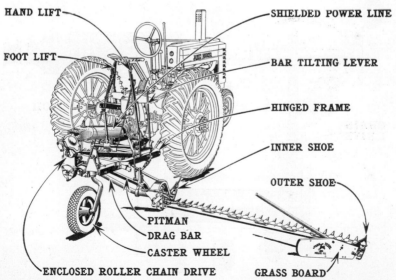

Figure 204—Tractor-driven mower, attached to general-purpose type of tractor.

clutch properly adjusted. Clutch should be tight enough to do ordinary work without slipping, but loose enough to slip easily if clogging occurs. Extreme care should be exercised in making this adjustment—directions furnished by the manufacturer should be followed closely.

When the cutter bar of the tractor mowers shown hits an obstruction, a spring release unlatches and permits the bar to swing back, protecting the mower against breakage.

Serving as a latch, the spring release holds the bar in cutting position under all normal conditions but releases when an unusual pressure or shock is encountered. The amount of pressure required to cause the lock to release is adjusted by tightening or loosening a spring tension. The operator must be careful to avoid setting this spring too tight, as such a condition may cause breakage should the lock fail to release.

After the bar swings back, it may be returned to operating position by backing the tractor.

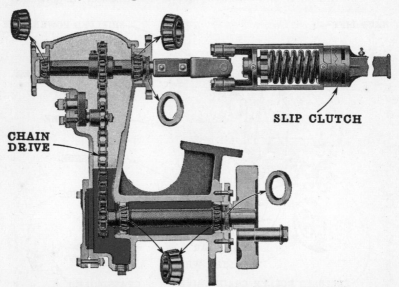

SLIP CLUTCH

CHAIN DRIVE

Figure 205—Cross-sectional view of tractor mower showing main drive, clutch, and bearings. Color indicates oiling of enclosed mechanism.

For ordinary field operation, the foot lift raises the bar high enough to meet field conditions. If the bar must be raised higher, the hand lever may be used. The tilting lever controls the tilt of the bar in relation to the ground. In some conditions, it is necessary to raise the guard points higher than in others. The tilting lever provides this adjustment.

Hydraulic control through the remote cylinder may be applied to the tractor mower to raise and lower the cutter bar and to vary the height of cutting as required. Figure 206 shows the remote cylinder attached to the power mower.

Thorough oiling and careful attention to proper adjustment and repair will increase the efficiency and lengthen the life of a tractor mower.

Questions

1. *How is the tractor mower driven?*
2. *What is the purpose of the slip clutch? Why is it necessary that it be properly adjusted?*
3. *What happens when the cutter bar hits an obstruction?*
4. *How is the bar raised? Tilted?*

Figure 206—Power mower with hydraulic control cylinder attached.

Chapter XIX.

HAY HANDLING EQUIPMENT

Hay is a highly perishable crop. It must be cut at the right time, cured properly, and handled carefully from field to feeding rack if its maximum feeding value is to be retained. This is especially true of legume hay, such as alfalfa, clover, and soybean. Timothy, blue grass, and wild hay are less perishable and do not require such exacting methods of handling.

Since the greater part of the feeding value of legume hay is contained in the leaves, every operation in curing and handling must have as its main purpose conservation of the leaves, along with thorough curing of the stems. High-grade legume hay should have its natural green color, should be fresh and sweet, and should retain all of the leaves on the stems without shattering when the hay is handled.

Modern machines and modern methods of handling hay are used to great advantage in increasing the feeding and market

Figure 207—The automatic press speeds the hay from windrow to bale and reduces time and labor cost.

value and decreasing the cost of producing legume hay. The side-delivery rake is considered necessary to the proper curing of legume hay. The hay loader is recognized as a labor-saver and cost-reducer that speeds up hay making.

The hay press is gaining in popularity from year to year. While baling does not improve the quality of the hay, it does preserve its quality, makes it readily available for feeding or for sale. When we consider that loose hay in the stack or mow weighs from 4 to 5 pounds per cubic foot, and that hay baled under extreme pressure will weigh as much as 40 pounds per cubic foot, it is readily understood why baled hay is easier to store, handle, and transport, and why it feeds out with less waste than bulk or loose hay.

Modern hay presses have done much to preserve the quality of the hay and to speed the harvesting of this highly perishable crop. The automatic pick-up baler (Fig. 207) cuts cost in both time and labor and makes baling hay a one-man job.

The pick-up hay chopper meets the requirements of the farmer who wants to chop his field-cured hay for economical

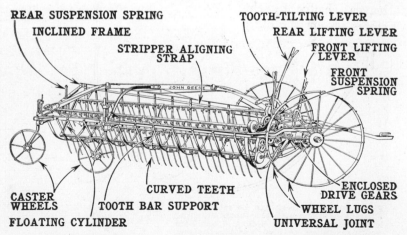

REAR SUSPENSION SPRING   TOOTH-TILTING LEVER
 INCLINED FRAME   REAR LIFTING LEVER
   STRIPPER ALIGNING   FRONT LIFTING
     STRAP   LEVER
           FRONT
           SUSPENSION
           SPRING

            ENCLOSED
       CURVED TEETH   DRIVE GEARS
CASTER
WHEELS TOOTH BAR SUPPORT WHEEL LUGS
FLOATING CYLINDER   UNIVERSAL JOINT

Figure 208—Side-delivery rake with the more important parts named.

storage in mow or stack, or to ensile his green hay crops for a succulent winter feed.

Side-Delivery Rakes

When the hay is cut, the flow of ground moisture is shut off, but the plant is full of water. The problem, then, is to reduce the moisture to a safe percentage for storing, and to do this in the shortest possible time.

The leaves, or tops, are left exposed to the sunlight, as they fall back over the mower cutter bar. If allowed to remain in this position very long, the leaves dry up and shatter. When this happens, the natural flow of moisture from stems to leaves is stopped and the moisture is "bottled up" in the stems. This results in unevenly cured hay.

The function of the side-delivery rake (Figs. 208 and 210) is to lift the hay from the swaths and place it in loose, fluffy windrows with the green leaves inside, protected from the sun's rays. The leaves, shaded by the stems, are cured rapidly

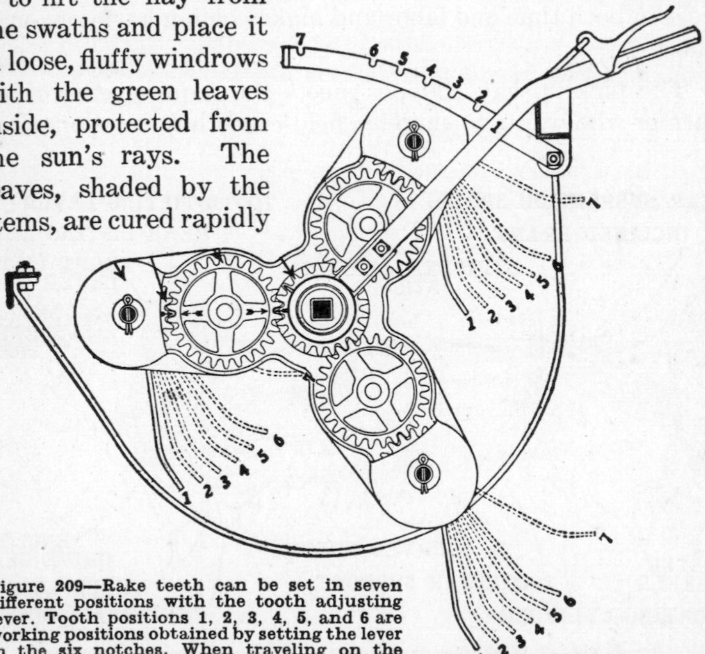

Figure 209—Rake teeth can be set in seven different positions with the tooth adjusting lever. Tooth positions 1, 2, 3, 4, 5, and 6 are working positions obtained by setting the lever in the six notches. When traveling on the road, the lever should be moved to position 7.

by the free circulation of air through the windrows. They retain their fresh, green color and the stems are thoroughly cured for storing.

If rainy weather catches the hay in the windrow, it is often necessary to turn it several times before it is thoroughly cured and ready for storing. When turning the windrow is advisable, the left front wheel of the rake is set in on the axle to allow enough of the reel to extend beyond for turning the windrow upside down when the left-hand wheel is run next to the right-hand edge of the windrow. This operation inverts the windrow, placing it bottom-side up on dry stubble with the damp hay exposed for curing.

Field Operation. Side-delivery rakes, once they are adjusted to suit field conditions, are easy to operate. The operator simply drives his team or tractor and oils his machine when necessary.

The most important adjustment is setting the teeth in the proper position, or angle, in relation to the surface of the ground. This is done with the tooth-adjusting lever, with which it is possible to set the teeth in six different working positions (see Fig. 209). The teeth should always be set as high as possible and still pick up all of the hay. This setting

Figure 210—A field scene, showing two side-delivery rakes, hitched tandem, at work with a general-purpose tractor.

causes the curved teeth to lift the hay gently, leaving the windrow as loose as possible and permitting free circulation of air.

In traveling on the road, the tooth-adjusting lever should be moved to notch seven. In this position, the teeth are raised above the strippers out of danger of being bent by hitting obstructions.

The front lifting lever should be adjusted so that the front end of the reel is low enough to pick up the hay, but never so low that the teeth strike the ground. A trial with the lever in the center notch will usually give an indication as to the position in which it should be set.

The rear lifting lever is properly set when the rear end of the reel is slightly higher than the front end. This aids in making the windrow loose and fluffy.

Care Important. When starting a new side-delivery rake, or when using one that has been stored, it is a good plan to turn the reel by hand to be sure it revolves freely and that the teeth do not strike the stripper bars. Then throw the rake into gear and turn the wheel by hand to see that the tooth bars and gears work freely. Breakage of parts which results in serious delay can be avoided by taking these precautions before entering the field.

All wearing parts should be oiled regularly. An occasional thorough inspection for loose nuts, worn bolts, and other parts will add to the efficiency of the side-delivery rake.

Sulky Rakes

The sulky, or dump rake, used in practically every section of the country, is built in both horse- and tractor-drawn types. Since the horse-drawn type is more common on farms today, a rake of that type will be used for discussion in this text. While it is easy to operate and adjust, many farmers work at a disadvantage when a slight adjustment would produce much better results.

The first requirement for good work is proper hitching. The rake shown in Fig. 211 is designed to work with the tongue 31 inches from the ground, measuring underneath at the front end. If this position is not maintained, the rake teeth will set at an improper angle, resulting in inferior work. If the tongue is too high, the teeth will have difficulty in clearing the hay after dumping; if too low, the teeth may fail to gather all of the hay.

Adjustments. Slight pressure on a foot trip lever causes the dump rods to engage in the wheel ratchets resulting in dumping of the rake. After the rake teeth have cleared the hay and started downward, they may be forced down quicker and held in position on the ground by pressure on the foot lever. An adjustment is provided at the hinge in this lever by which the wear can be taken up. If an adjustment is not made when the hinge becomes worn, the rake will be dumped with difficulty.

The height to which the teeth rise when the rake is dumped is controlled by adjusting a snubbing block bolt, located on the frame to the rear of the seat spring. If the rake rises too high and, consequently, does not get back to work as soon as it should, the block bolt must be screwed out of the block one or more turns. Turning the block bolt down permits the rake to rise higher when dumped.

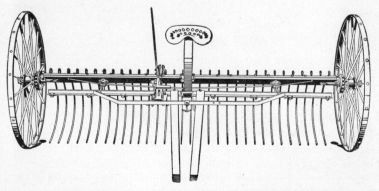

Figure 211—The sulky rake is used in practically every section of the country.

If the rake repeats when it is dumped, the tension on trip spring is insufficient to hold the dump rod out of the wheel ratchets. More tension is produced by turning down the nut on the trip spring bolt.

When the wheel ratchets or dump rods become worn, the wheels and rods can be reversed, giving double wear.

Keep Nuts Tight. Because of the vibration attendant to raking, it is necessary that all nuts be kept tight. It is a good plan to go over the rake at regular intervals for this purpose.

Oil, used liberally on axles and wearing parts, will make for good work and lengthen the life of a dump rake.

Hay Loaders

One of the greatest labor- and time-saving machines for the farmer is the hay loader. It displaces hand pitching—one of the hardest and most tiresome jobs on the farm—speeds up hay making and cuts production costs. The hay loader is needed on every farm where the hay is loaded in the field

Figure 212—Building a load with the raker bar-cylinder loader.

and put directly into the barns or hauled to stacks. Ten to fifteen acres of hay justify the purchase of a hay loader.

While most manufacturers build loaders of several designs, including heavy-duty types especially for loading green crops, the raker bar-cylinder type is generally recognized as the most efficient. For this reason, a loader of this type (Fig. 213) will be used for study of the hay loader.

In operation, the teeth on the floating gathering cylinder "comb" the stubble to pick up all of the clean hay and pass it on to the deck. Here, the slow moving raker bars elevate the hay to the adjustable extension deck, or gate, from which it passes to the rack.

The most important factor in the satisfactory operation of a loader is the proper setting of the gathering cylinder. It does the best work when it is set in the highest position

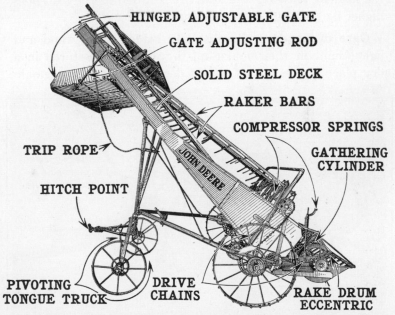

Figure 213—Combination raker bar-cylinder loader with the more important parts named.

in which it will do a clean job of raking. If set too high it misses some of the hay; if too low, it gathers trash and the spring teeth scratch the ground, throwing dust into the hay. Height of the gathering cylinder is varied by moving the position of the hand nut on the adjusting rod on each side of the loader. A spring placed behind each crank gives a floating action to the cylinder. In moving from field to field, the gathering cylinder should be raised to highest position by running the hand nuts all the way down on the adjusting rods.

The loader should be hitched as close to the rack as possible, but not so close as to cause it to strike the corners of the rack in turning.

The carrier extension or gate can be lowered for starting the load by releasing the lever. It is raised as the load goes higher by pushing up on the center of the gate.

Care of Loaders. Because hay loaders have wood and light chain in their make-up, they should be stored in a dry place if possible. If the loader is permitted to remain

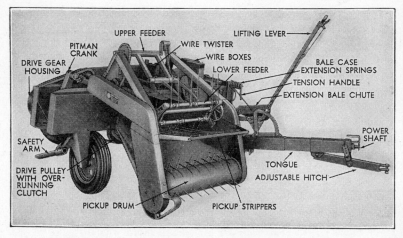

Figure 214—Important parts of the automatic baler are named above.

in the open, the rain and sun shorten its life and increase upkeep costs. Shelter should be provided whenever possible. The foretruck on the loader shown may be folded back to reduce height of deck for ease in storing. A long lever at front frame controls this adjustment.

The usual admonition regarding thorough oiling of farm machines and keeping all nuts tight can be repeated for all hay loaders. Slack seasons furnish an opportunity to overhaul the hay loader along with other farm machines.

Hay Balers

As mentioned previously, the modern automatic pick-up baler has done much to reduce time and labor costs in harvesting the hay crop. The earlier windrow pick-up presses, in common with the stationary or continuous type, were limited in their capacity by the speed and dexterity of the tying crew; by eliminating the slow and tedious job of hand tying which required the services of two men, the modern pick-up baler is a real time- and labor-saver in harvesting a perishable crop which must be done when other farm work is pressing for attention.

The baler shown is an automatic wire-tying, pick-up baler operated by the power take-off of a two-plow tractor. In operation, the windrow is lifted by the pick-up drum, passed onto the feeders and into the transverse baling case, where it is compressed, in sliced charges, against pre-formed wire loops. Subsequent charges are added, until the bale reaches a weight of approximately 75 pounds, at which time the twisting mechanism is tripped and the tying cycle begins. Both ties are twisted, the twist is cut in the center, and the parts forming the completed bale are double kinked to prevent slippage. The remaining twists, also double kinked, form the loops for the following bale.

While the automatic baler does its work in a direct, comparatively simple manner, certain basic considerations must be observed. All hay should be windrowed with a side-delivery rake for uniform feeding to the baling case. Since proper timing of reciprocating parts is of great importance, it is well for the operator to familiarize himself with the function of all parts before attempting high speed operation. The operator's manual, which accompanies the new baler, should be followed carefully if the baler is to give the fullest service. Special attention should be given to proper lubrication of all parts.

The hay baler, shown in Fig. 215, is of the continuous type, a type in common use throughout the United States today. In operation, the charge of hay, placed into the hopper by the feeder on the platform, is forced into the chamber by the feeder head.

Grooved blocks, placed at regular intervals by the operator, determine the size of the bales. Baling ties are slipped through the grooves and fastened securely around the bale. As the bales are forced from the baler, the blocks drop to the ground.

Operation and Adjustment. Before starting the baler, inspect the entire outfit carefully for loose bolts. Oil all

Figure 215—The light power baler is in wide use for stationary baling.

moving parts including main bearings for large gears, main shaft and intermediate gear shaft bearings, and crank-pin bearing. Turn the press by hand to be sure all parts are running freely. Adjust tension levers so that height inside the case is from 1/2 to 3/4 of an inch less than the height of a standard bale.

Extra care in feeding, to be sure that small charges of uniform size (6 to 8 pounds of hay) are placed into the feeder, will result in neat bales of uniform shape and size. When dropping division blocks, be sure that the block driver on nose of feeder head strikes the block squarely to insure positive drive of the block.

Baling ties should be reasonably tight, otherwise much of the work done in compressing the bale will be wasted.

In operation, all bearings should be oiled at regular intervals six to eight times daily. A daily inspection for loose bolts and worn parts is an important responsibility of the operator.

Field Hay Chopper. The advent of modern field hay

Figure 216—The field hay chopper at work in field-cured hay.

choppers has changed the haying procedure on many farms.

Chopping hay in the field not only reduces labor of handling, but insures hay of higher feeding value since practically all of the leaves—the real feeding value of the crop—are preserved.

Many farmers and dairymen have turned to green legume silage as a source of highly palatable winter stock feed. Most farmers who ensile these crops choose to use the

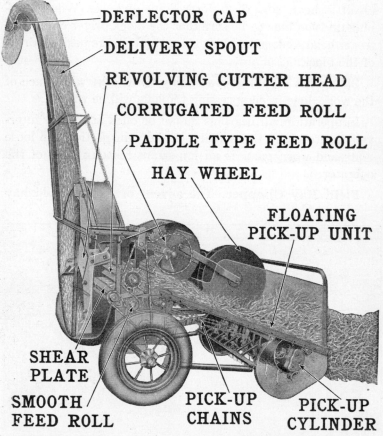

DEFLECTOR CAP

DELIVERY SPOUT

REVOLVING CUTTER HEAD

CORRUGATED FEED ROLL

PADDLE TYPE FEED ROLL

HAY WHEEL

FLOATING
PICK-UP UNIT

SHEAR
PLATE

SMOOTH
FEED ROLL

PICK-UP
CHAINS

PICK-UP
CYLINDER

Figure 217—Phantom view of the pick-up hay chopper showing progress
of windrow through the machine.

first cutting which is the least desirable as field-cured hay and which is ready for cutting early in the season when the weather makes field curing uncertain.

In operation (see Fig. 217), the field hay chopper picks up the windrow, passes it on to the feed rolls which feed it into the cutting mechanism. In the chopper shown, four radial knives working against a shear plate, cut the material into proper length. Steel paddles, on the outer ends of the knife holders, throw and blow the cut material through the delivery spout to the wagon or truck.

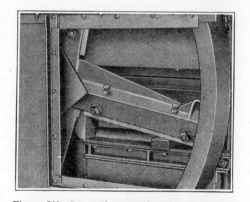

The adjustment and operation of the hay chopper are comparatively simple, yet certain fundamentals must be observed.

The floating pickup unit should be set so that runners just touch the ground. The pick-up unit set in this position is free to float over high spots in the field and do a good job of picking up the windrow.

Figure 218—Inspection panel removed to show position and setting of radial knives and shear plate.

The continued efficient operation of the hay chopper depends to a great degree upon the condition of the radial knives and shear plate. These should

Figure 219—Sharpening the shear plate on the tractor-operated knife grinder.

be inspected at regular intervals and sharpened when necessary. Alignment of these parts should be checked and compensating adjustments made. Special care should be taken to keep all nuts tight.

Thorough lubrication of all parts is especially important in high-speed equipment of this type.

Questions

1. What qualities do you consider high-grade hay must have?
2. What legumes are grown in your community?
3. What is meant by "air curing" hay? Is this method used extensively in your community?
4. What is the function of the side-delivery rake?
5. How should the teeth of a side-delivery rake be set in relation to the ground surface?
6. What are the principal adjustments necessary on a dump rake?
7. What is the advantage of reversible wheels and dump rods?
8. How large an acreage of hay justifies the purchase of a hay loader?
9. How should the gathering cylinder be set for efficient work?
10. When is the extension carrier used and what are its advantages?
11. Why should hay loaders be put under shelter when not in use?
12. What are the advantages of baling hay for feeding or for market?
13. What are the advantages of chopping hay?
14. Name the important points in servicing the hay chopper.

Part Six
SOIL FERTILITY

Soil is the source of food that sustains mankind. It is productive so long as it contains sufficient quantities of all the essential plant-food elements, and so long as the right methods are observed by the farmer in working his land.

The supply of plant-food elements in the soil is not inexhaustible. Like a bank account, it becomes depleted if the amount withdrawn is greater than the amount deposited.

With the removal of each crop, the soil surrenders some of its fertility. If an equal amount of fertility is returned by man, productiveness is maintained.

Chapter XX.
MANURE SPREADERS AND LOADERS

Experience has proved to farmers in every section of the country that barnyard manure is of great value as a soil fertilizer and a factor in permanent agriculture. The insistent

Figure 220—The modern manure spreader is a valuable soil-builder.

urgings of scientists and farm experts have moved farmers to try a regular plan of covering their fields with the manure and waste vegetable matter from their barns and feed yards. The results have proved gratifying and, as a general rule, farmers value highly the manure that was once considered a useless by-product of farming that was to be disposed of in the easiest possible manner or permitted to rot and waste away in piles about the barnyard.

One of the major reasons for the wastage of manure in the early days of agricultural expansion was the great amount of hand labor required to get it distributed evenly over the fields. The hard work of pitching into high wagon boxes, unloading into piles, and spreading by hand or spreading direct from the load was distasteful even to the farmer who was most conscientious about maintaining the fertility of his fields. The result was a more or less general laxity in conserving the manure that is now valued so highly.

Figure 221—The push-type loader does a fine job of cleaning up manure in barns and feed lots

The following graphs, furnished through courtesy of the Ohio State University, supply interesting facts about the value of manure in maintaining soil fertility and, in addition, show results obtained from various methods of handling manure.

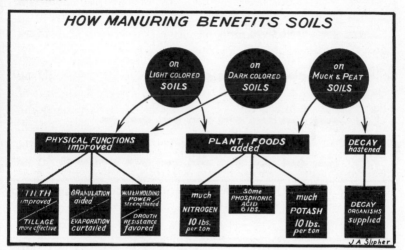

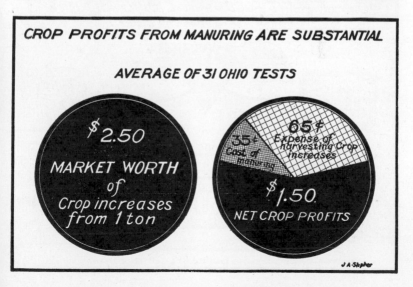

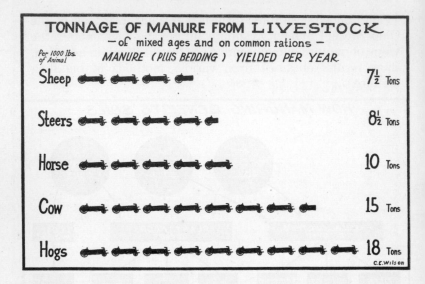

TONNAGE OF MANURE FROM LIVESTOCK
— of mixed ages and on common rations —

Per 1000 lbs. of Animal

MANURE (PLUS BEDDING) YIELDED PER YEAR

Sheep — 7½ Tons

Steers — 8½ Tons

Horse — 10 Tons

Cow — 15 Tons

Hogs — 18 Tons

C.E.Wilson

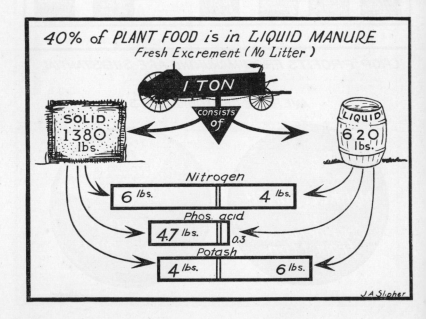

40% of PLANT FOOD is in LIQUID MANURE
Fresh Excrement (No Litter)

I TON consists of

SOLID 1380 lbs.

LIQUID 620 lbs.

Nitrogen
6 lbs.   4 lbs.

Phos. acid
4.7 lbs.   0.3

Potash
4 lbs.   6 lbs.

J.A.Slipher

STRAW IS STRONG WATER ABSORBENT

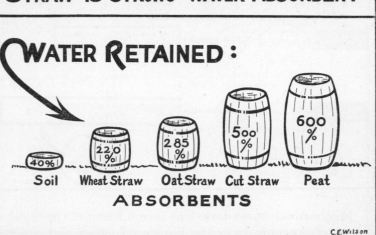

WATER RETAINED:

| 40% | 220% | 285% | 500% | 600% |
| Soil | Wheat Straw | Oat Straw | Cut Straw | Peat |

ABSORBENTS

C.E.Wilson

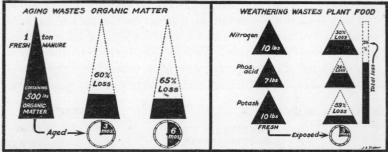

AGING WASTES ORGANIC MATTER

1 ton FRESH MANURE

CONTAINING 500 lbs ORGANIC MATTER

60% Loss — Aged → 3 mos.

65% Loss — 6 mos.

WEATHERING WASTES PLANT FOOD

Nitrogen 10 lbs — 30% Loss

Phos. acid 7 lbs — 24% Loss

Potash 10 lbs — 59% Loss

FRESH — Exposed → 3 mos.

Total loss 39%

J.A.Slipher

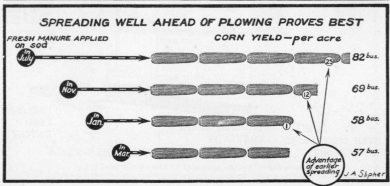

SPREADING WELL AHEAD OF PLOWING PROVES BEST

FRESH MANURE APPLIED on sod

CORN YIELD — per acre

In July		25	82 bus.
In Nov		12	69 bus.
In Jan.		1	58 bus.
In Mar.			57 bus.

Advantage of earlier spreading

J.A.Slipher

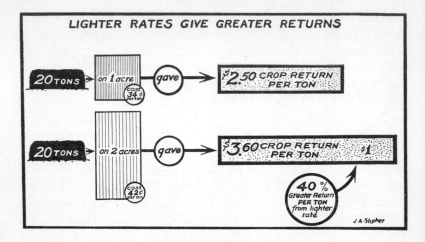

Mechanical Spreaders. The introduction of the manure spreader not only gave the farmer an easier and quicker method of spreading his barnyard manure, but it also paved the way for a more concentrated effort on the part of agricultural leaders to impress upon him the value of its use in increasing crop production. Winning the farmer to the use of the spreader was comparatively easy when both the labor-saving and crop-producing features were pointed out to him.

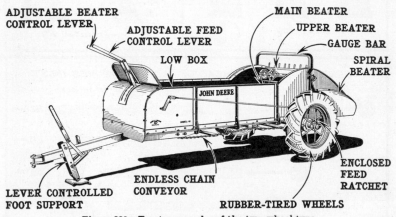

Figure 222—Tractor spreader of the two-wheel type.

Today, the great majority of farms are equipped with some type of manure spreader. Farmers are adding to their profits and building up their soils by utilizing the manure that was once wasted. The general practice is to spread the manure on the fields as it accumulates, thus getting the full benefit of all the plant-food elements.

To be most effective, manure must be spread evenly over the entire surface of the field. If it is deposited in bunches, part of the soil is without fertilizer and part is oversupplied. If the manure has a large amount of straw in it, difficulty is experienced in plowing and cultivating spots where it is bunched. The proper loading and operating of the manure spreader will overcome or lessen the possibilities of uneven spreading, provided the spreader is constructed properly.

Types of Spreaders. The tractor spreader, shown in Fig. 222, is of the two-wheel type, with front end supported by the tractor. The direct hitch serves two important purposes: it reduces the over-all length of the outfit, permitting the operator to work in close quarters, and it distributes

Figure 223—Returning fertility and humus to the soil with a horse-drawn spreader.

the weight over spreader and tractor wheels for ample traction in wet or slippery fields and feed lots.

Operating levers are placed on the spreader for easy accessibility from the tractor seat. The stand or supporting foot which supports the spreader when not in use is raised or lowered from the tractor seat by means of the lever on the stub pole.

The three beaters serve to break up or shred the manure and distribute it in the quantity required. The upper and main beaters shred the manure; the spiral beater deposits it evenly over the entire width, making a well-defined line beyond the drive wheels.

The manure is carried back to the beaters by a steel slat conveyor, the speed of which is controlled by the feed lever placed well forward on the spreader. From five to twenty loads can be spread per acre, according to the setting of the feed lever.

The operator must be sure to keep the feed lever forward in neutral, whenever the machine is not in gear or whenever the beaters are not operating. If the feed lever is left in

Figure 224—The modern manure loader is a real time- and labor-saver in loading the manure spreader.

operating position when starting to the field with a load, the conveyor forces the load back against the beater, resulting in breakage in some part of the feed mechanism. The feed lever should be thrown into neutral, also, when turning sharply while spreading.

With the control lever, the operator shifts the main drive chain so that it is in contact with the large drive sprocket. The three beaters are driven by two chains, both of which are set into action by the drive sprocket. The beaters should not be put into gear in this manner while the machine is in motion. The control lever should be moved to the rear only when the spreader is standing still.

A four-wheel horse-drawn spreader, similar in construction to the tractor-drawn spreader discussed above, is shown at work in Fig. 223. Levers are placed for convenient operation from the driver's seat.

Building the Load. In building the load, it is best to start at the front of the loader and finish at the beater end. The shredding process, which is the work of the beaters, imposes less strain on the spreader when the load is built in this man-

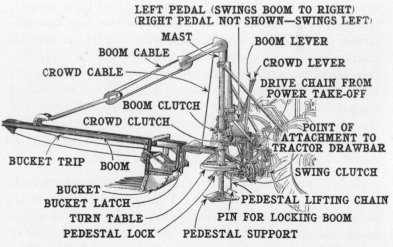

Figure 225—The manure loader with important operating parts indicated.

ner, resulting in lighter draft and less wear on the machine.

Manure Loaders. Cleaning up manure in feed lots and around buildings has always been a problem for feeders and dairymen. Valuable as manure is, many farmers have been forced by pressure of other farm work to let it lie unspread, wasting its plant-food elements until time could be found to haul it to the field.

Modern manure loaders (Figs. 221 and 224) speed up the work of loading spreaders and relieve the operator of the hard, disagreeable job of pitching manure by hand.

The rear mounted, pedestal type manure loader, shown in detail in Fig. 225, is mounted at the rear of the tractor to provide an unobstructed view of the work. The operator, seated upon the tractor, has all operating controls for moving the boom and bucket within easy reach at all times. An automatic trip near end of boom releases the load.

In transporting or in moving from set to set, the pedestal is raised by the boom, telescoping into the mast. The push-type loader, shown in Fig. 226 with principal parts named, is a fast, easily-operated loader, ideal for the "one tractor" farmer since the tractor equipped with this loader may be used for hauling the spreader as well as for loading. The push-type loader has a distinct advantage in working in close quarters in feed lots and sheds. Like all modern tractor-mounted equipment, the push-type loader is controlled from the tractor seat. Power for the loader shown is supplied direct from the flywheel of the tractor so that the loader may be operated whenever the tractor engine is running.

Highly important in the operation of the manure loader is proper lubrication of all parts. Time devoted to an occasional check-up to make certain that all parts are in alignment and all connections tight will repay the operator in fast, efficient work.

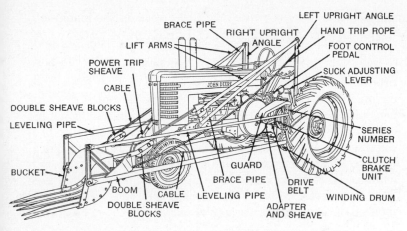

Figure 226—The push-type loader showing detail of construction.

Questions

1. What relation has soil fertility to the production of food?
2. Name the types of fertilizer used on farms in your community.
3. What are the advantages of using a manure spreader over hand-spreading methods?
4. How should manure be spread to be of most value?
5. How would you build a load of manure for best results?
6. How is the quantity to be spread per acre controlled?
7. Why is thorough oiling important?
8. What percent of farms in your neighborhood are equipped with manure spreaders?
9. What advantages does the modern manure loader offer to feeders and dairymen?
10. Describe two types of manure loaders and tell how each is operated?
11. What servicing operations are especially important?

Chapter XXI.

LIME AND FERTILIZER SOWERS

In every section of the country, there are soils that would produce better crops with the application of lime, the proper commercial fertilizer, or a combination of both. Sour or acid soils that have been depleted of their lime by constant cropping or poor drainage can be rejuvenated and their productivity greatly increased by the application of lime. "Worn-out" soils can be brought back to a productive state with commercial fertilizers and lime applied in correct amounts. The lime sower affords the easiest and most economical method of distributing these materials.

Lime and fertilizer distributors are made with two types of feeds—the star force-feeds that handle from 50 to 5000 pounds per acre, and the rotary wing feeds that sow from 200 to 8000 pounds per acre. This latter type, when equipped with pneumatic tires, is used for distributing calcium chloride, cinders, salt, and other materials on roads.

Figure 227—Spreading a uniform layer of lime with a modern lime and fertilizer distributor. Half the feeds have been closed, to finish the job.

Spreads Evenly. Uniform spreading of the correct amount of material per acre is the first requisite of a good lime sower. Bunching or skipping brings unsatisfactory results.

Fig. 227 shows a lime and fertilizer sower which spreads lime or fertilizer evenly in any amount from 200 to 8000 pounds per acre. The operator's only responsibilities are filling the hopper, setting his machine to sow the desired amount per acre, and driving the team or tractor. Two levers on the rear of the hopper (see Fig. 227) provide adjustment for quantity to be distributed. Half the feeds may be shut off when sowing a narrow strip.

Agitator Keeps Material Flowing. A revolving agitator in the bottom of the hopper keeps the lime or fertilizer flowing evenly through the feed openings. Its purpose is to prevent clogging or bridging of the material and the consequent skipping that would result.

Figure 228—Laying a ribbon of fertilizer in the plow-sole with the plow-sole fertilizer attachment.

Scattering boards, hung beneath the feed openings, aid in even distribution. The material is deflected and spread as it falls from the feeds. These boards also aid in more even distribution on windy days. Adjustment up or down is provided by a chain on each board.

If properly cared for, a lime sower should last for many years and prove to be a profitable investment.

The plow-sole fertilizer shown in Fig. 228, while a comparatively new development, is gaining acceptance rapidly wherever it is desired to place fertilizer in the bottom of the seedbed where it is available as root systems develop. The plow-sole fertilizer is easily attached to the plow and requires but little attention other than keeping the hopper filled. Quantity of fertilizer distributed can be varied to meet soil requirements.

In addition to the fertilizer distributors described above, a simple lime-spreading attachment for spreading lime in practically any quantity desired, is available for many modern manure spreaders, thereby making the manure spreader doubly useful in preserving soil fertility.

Questions

1. *What are the advantages of using a lime or fertilizer sower? Discuss methods of sowing.*
2. *Why is even distribution important?*
3. *What is the purpose of the agitator?*
4. *Why is a scattering board used?*
5. *Are lime and fertilizer sowers used in your community?*
6. *What are the advantages of the plow-sole fertilizer attachment?*

Decimal Parts of an Inch

1/64—.015625	23/64—.359375	43/64— .671875
1/32—.03125	3/8—.375	11/16— .6875
3/64—.046875		45/64— .703125
1/16—.0625	25/64—.390625	23/32— .71875
	13/32—.40625	
5/64—.078125		47/64— .734375
3/32—.09375		3/4— .750
	27/64—.421875	
7/64—.109375	7/16—.4375	49/64— .765625
1/8—.125		25/32— .78125
	29/64—.453125	
9/64—.140625	15/32—.46875	51/64— .796875
5/32—.15625		13/16— .8125
	31/64—.484375	
11/64—.171875	1/2—.500	53/64— .828125
3/16—.1875		27/32— .84375
	33/64—.515625	
13/64—.203125	17/32—.53125	55/64— .859375
7/32—.21875		7/8— .875
	35/64—.546875	
15/64—.234375	9/16—.5625	57/64— .890625
1/4—.250		29/32— .90625
	37/64—.578125	
17/64—.265625	19/32—.59375	59/64— .921875
9/32—.28125		15/16— .9375
	39/64—.609375	
19/64—.296875	5/8—.625	61/64— .953125
5/16—.3125		31/32— .96875
	41/64—.640625	
21/64—.328125	21/32—.65625	63/64— .984375
11/32—.34375		1—1.00000

Sizes of Wire

A. S. & W. STEEL WIRE GAUGE	SIZES OF WIRE		Weight One Mile Pounds	Pounds per Foot	Feet to Pound
	Common Fractions	Decimally			
1		.2830	1128.0	.2136	4.681
	9/32	.28125	1114.0	.211	
2		.2625	970.4	.1838	5.441
	1/4	.250	880.2	.1667	
3		.2437	836.4	.1584	6.313
4		.2253	714.8	.1354	7.386
	7/32	.21875	673.9	.1276	
5		.2070	603.4	.1143	8.750
6		.1920	519.2	.0983	10.17
	3/16	.1875	495.1	.0937	
7		.1770	441.2	.0835	11.97
8		.1620	369.6	.070	14.29
	5/32	.15625	343.8	.0651	
9		.1483	309.7	.0586	17.05
10		.1350	256.7	.0486	20.57
	1/8	.1250	220.0	.0416	
11		.1205	204.5	.0387	25.82
12		.1055	156.7	.0296	33.69
	3/32	.09375	123.8	.0234	
13		.0915	117.9	.0223	44.78
14		.0800	90.13	.0170	58.58
15		.0720	73.01	.0138	72.32
16	1/16	.0625	55.0	.0104	95.98
17		.0540	41.07	.0077	128.6
18		.0475	31.77	.006	166.2
19		.0410	23.67	.0044	223.0
20		.0348	17.05	.0032	309.6

Miles Traveled in Plowing an Acre

Width of Furrow, Inches	Miles
10	9-9/10
11	9
12	8-1/4
13	7-1/2
14	7
15	6-1/2
16	6-1/6

Acreage per Mile of Various Widths

Width	Acres	Width	Acres
1 foot	0.121	15 feet	1.815
5 feet	0.605	16 feet	1.936
8 feet	0.968	18 feet	2.178
10 feet	1.21	20 feet	2.42
12 feet	1.452	24 feet	2.904
14 feet	1.694	25 feet	3.025

Miles Traveled in Planting an Acre—3'6" Rows

1-Row Planter	2.34 miles
2-Row Planter	1.17 miles
3-Row Planter	.78 miles

Acres Planted in Traveling One Mile—3'6" Rows

1-Row Planter	.42 acres
2-Row Planter	.84 acres
3-Row Planter	1.26 acres

There are 10,667 stalks in an acre planted in 3'6" rows, three stalks to the hill, hills 3'6" apart, or drilled one stalk every 14 inches.

There are 3,556 hills in an acre planted in 3'6" rows, hills 3'6" apart.

U. S. Government Land Measure

A township—36 sections, each a mile square.

A section—640 acres.

A quarter section—half a mile square, 160 acres.

An eighth section, half a mile long, north and south, and a quarter of a mile wide—80 acres.

A sixteenth section, a quarter of a mile square—40 acres.

The sections are all numbered 1 to 36, commencing at the northeast corner.

The sections are divided into quarters, which are named by the cardinal points. The quarters are divided in the same way. The description of a forty-acre lot would read: The south half of the west half of the southwest quarter of section 1 in township 24, north of range 7 west, or as the case might be, and sometimes will fall short and sometimes overrun the number of acres it is supposed to contain.

NOTE—In most of the western states, where all of the land was laid out by the Government, all titles, except in city lots, are passed by description, as under the Government survey, and there a square of 6 miles, or 36 square miles, is one township.

Land Measure

To find the number of acres in a body of land, multiply the length by the width (in rods) and divide the product by 160. When the opposite sides are unequal, add them, and take half the sum for the mean length or width.

To Measure Corn in Cribs

Ear corn of good quality, measured when settled, will hold out at $2\frac{1}{2}$ cubic feet to the bushel. Allowance should be made for snapped corn, corn that is poorly husked, or otherwise inferior in quality, which will hold out at more than $2\frac{1}{2}$ cubic feet per bushel.

Rule—At $2\frac{1}{2}$ cubic feet to the bushel, divide the cubic feet in crib by $2\frac{1}{2}$, or multiply by 2 and divide by 5.

To Find the Number of Tons of Hay in a Mow

Multiply the length by the width by the height (all in feet) and divide by 400 to 500 depending on the kind of hay and how long it has been in the mow.

To Find the Number of Tons of Hay in a Stack

Multiply the overthrow (the distance from the ground on one side over the top of the stack to the ground on the other side) by the length by the width (all in feet); multiply by 3; divide by 10, and then divide by 500 to 600, depending upon the length of time the hay has been in the stack.

Capacity of Corn Cribs. (Dry Corn)

(Height, 10 Feet)

Length	$\frac{1}{2}$	1	12	14	16	18	20	22	24	28	32	36	48	64
Width 6	12	24	288	366	384	432	480	528	576	672	768	864	1152	1536
6$\frac{1}{4}$	12	25	300	350	400	450	500	550	600	700	800	900	1200	1599
6$\frac{1}{2}$	13	26	312	364	416	468	520	572	624	728	832	936	1248	1664
6$\frac{3}{4}$	13	27	324	378	432	486	540	594	648	756	864	972	1296	1728
7	14	28	336	392	448	504	560	616	672	784	896	1008	1344	1792
7$\frac{1}{4}$	14	29	348	406	464	522	580	638	696	812	928	1044	1392	1856
7$\frac{1}{2}$	15	30	360	420	480	540	600	660	720	840	960	1080	1440	1920
7$\frac{3}{4}$	15	31	372	434	496	558	620	682	744	868	992	1116	1488	1984
8	16	32	384	448	512	576	640	704	768	896	1024	1152	1536	2048
8$\frac{1}{2}$	17	34	408	476	544	612	680	748	816	952	1088	1224	1632	2176
9	18	36	432	504	576	648	720	792	864	1008	1152	1296	1728	2304
10	20	40	480	560	640	720	800	880	960	1120	1280	1440	1920	2560

The length is found in top line, the width in left-hand column—the height being taken at 10 ft. Thus, a crib 24 ft. long, 7$\frac{1}{2}$ ft. wide and 10 ft. high, will hold 720 bushels of ear corn, reckoning 2$\frac{1}{2}$ cubic feet to hold a bushel. If not 10 ft. high, multiply by the given height and cut off right-hand figure. If above crib were only 7 ft. high, it would hold 720 x 7, equals 504(0) bu., etc. The same space will hold twice as much grain as ear corn. Thus, a crib that holds 720 bushels of ear corn will hold 720 x 2 equals 1440 bushels of grain.

Capacity of Silo

A silo, properly filled—that is, if the contents are made compact throughout—contains one ton of silage for every 50 cubic feet of space. To illustrate the economy of a silo to store stock feed as compared with a barn, a ton of hay requires 400 cubic feet of space. A farmer can easily figure how much a silo will contain by the following rules:

Multiply the square of the diameter by 0.7854, which will be the area of the circular floor. Multiply the area of the floor by the height, which will give the number of cubic feet. One cubic foot of silage weighs 40 lbs. Multiply the cubic feet by 40, and the result is the number of pounds of silage the silo will contain. Divide that by 2,000 to find the number of tons.

Diameter	Depth	Capacity in Tons	Acres to Fill 15 Tons to Acre	Cows It Will Keep 6 Months, 40 Lbs. per Day
10	20	31	2-1/3	8
12	20	45	3	12
12	24	54	3-3/5	15
12	28	63	4-1/5	17
14	22	67	4-1/2	18
14	24	74	5	20
14	28	87	5-2/3	24
14	30	93	6	26
16	24	96	6-2/5	27
16	26	104	7	29
16	30	120	8	33
18	30	152	10-1/5	42
18	36	183	12-1/3	50

Cistern Capacity

A cistern ten feet in diameter and nine feet deep will hold 168 barrels.

A cistern five feet in diameter will hold five and two-thirds barrels for every foot in depth.

A cistern six feet in diameter will hold six and three-fourths barrels for every foot in depth.

A cistern eight feet in diameter will hold nearly twelve barrels for every foot in depth.

A cistern nine feet in diameter will hold fifteen and one-half barrels for every foot in depth.

A cistern ten feet in diameter will hold eighteen and three-eighths barrels for every foot in depth.

To Find the Contents of Square Tanks in Gallons

Rule—Multiply the area of the bottom by the height in order to secure the cubic feet. Multiply the cubic feet by 7½ (exact 7.48) and the result will be the number of gallons. For the contents, in barrels, multiply the cubic feet by .2375.

To Find the Value of Articles Sold by the Ton

Multiply the number of pounds by the price per ton, point off 3 places and divide by 2.

To Find the Contents of Barrels and Casks in Gallons

Rule—Multiply the square of the mean diameter (in inches) by the depth (in inches) and the product by .0034.

Circles and Globes

To find the circumference of a circle, multiply the diameter by 3.1416.

To find the area of a circle, multiply the square of the diameter by .7854.

To find the surface of a globe, multiply the square of the diameter by 3.1416.

To find the solidity of a globe, multiply the cube of the diameter by .5236.

Commodity Weights and Measures

A pint's a pound—or very nearly—of the following: Water, wheat, butter, sugar, blackberries.

A gallon of milk weighs 8.6 pounds; cream, 8.4 pounds; 46½ quarts of milk weigh 100 pounds.

A keg of nails weighs 100 pounds. A barrel of flour weighs 196 pounds; of salt, 280 pounds; of beef, fish or pork, 200 pounds; cement (4 bags) 376 pounds.

Cotton in a standard bale weighs 480 pounds. A bushel of coal weighs 80 pounds.

A barrel of cement contains 3.8 cubic feet; of oil 42 gallons.

A barrel of dry commodities contains 7,056 cubic inches or 105 dry quarts.

A bushel, leveled, contains 2,150.42 cubic inches; a bushel heaped— 2,747.7 cubic inches. (Used to measure apples, potatoes, shelled corn in bin.)

A peck contains 537.605 cubic inches. A dry quart contains 67.201 cubic inches.

A board foot = 144 cubic inches; a cord contains 128 cubic feet.

Weights and Volumes of Water

One cubic inch of water weighs .036 pounds. One cubic foot weighs 62.5 pounds.

One cubic foot = 7.48 gallons. One pint (liquid) weighs 1.04 pounds. One gallon weighs 8.355 pounds. One gallon = 231 cubic inches. One liquid quart = 57.75 cubic inches.

Tables Convenient for Taking Inside Dimensions

A box 24 x 24 x 14.7 inches will hold a barrel of 31½ gallons.
A box 15 x 14 x 11 inches will hold 10 gallons.
A box 8¼ x 7 x 4 inches will hold a gallon.
A box 4 x 4 x 3.6 inches will hold a quart.
A box 16 x 12 x 11.2 inches will hold a bushel.
A box 12 x 11.2 x 8 inches will hold a half-bushel.
A box 7 x 6.4 x 12 inches will hold a peck.
A box 8.4 x 8 x 4 inches will hold a peck, or four dry quarts.
A box 6 x 5.6 x 4 inches deep will hold a half-gallon.

To Find Height of Tree or Building

Set up a stick and measure its shadow. Measure length of shadow of tree. Length of shadow of tree, times height of stick, divided by length of shadow of stick equals height of tree.

Common Measures

Long Measure

12	Inches	1	Foot
3	Feet	1	Yard
5½	Yards	1	Rod
320	Rods	1	Mile
1	Mile	5280	Feet

The following are also used:

1 Size.................1/3-Inch

(Used by Shoemakers)

1 Hand................4 Inches

(Used in measuring the height of horses.)

1 Fathom...............6 Feet

(Used in measuring depths at sea.)

Square Measure

144	Square Ins	1	Square Ft.
9	Square Ft	1	Square Yd.
30¼	Square Yds	1	Square Rd.
160	Square Rods	1	Acre
640	Acres	1	Square M.

An acre is equal to a square whose sides are 208.71 feet.

Surveyors' Square Measure

10,000 Square Links..1 Sq. Chain
10 Square Chains....1 Acre
10 Chains Square....10 Acres

Surveyor's Linear Measure

7.92 Inches.............1 Link
100 Links.............1 Chain
80 Chains............1 Mile
(Gunter's Chain is the unit and is 66 feet long.)

Dry Measure

2 Pints...............1 Quart
8 Quarts..............1 Peck
4 Pecks...............1 Bushel
1 Bushel contains 2150.42 cubic inches or approximately 1¼ cubic feet.

Liquid Measure

4 Gills...............1 Pint
2 Pints...............1 Quart
4 Quarts..............1 Gallon
1 Gallon contains 231 cubic inches.
1 Cubic Ft. equals 7½ gallons.

Cubic Measure

1728 Cubic Inches...1 Cubic Ft.
27 Cubic Feet.....1 Cubic Yd.
128 Cubic Feet....1 Cord

Number of Pounds to the Bushel

Alfalfa..:	60	Kafir Corn	56
Barley	48	Lime	80
Beans (White)	60	Malt	38
Bran	20	Millet Seed, Common	50
Buckwheat	48	Oats	32
Blue-Grass Seed	14	Onions	57
Clover Seed	60	Orchard Grass	14
Clover (Sweet)	60	Peas	60
Corn (Shelled)	56	Potatoes	60
Corn (In Ear)	70	Red Top Seed	14
Coal, Hard	80	Rye	56
Hubam Seed	60	Timothy Seed	45
Hungarian Grass Seed	45	Wheat	60

Belting Pointers

How to Find Length Required

When it is not convenient to measure with the tapeline the length required, apply the following rule: Add the diameter of the two pulleys together, divide the result by 2, and multiply the quotient by 3-1/4; then add this product to twice the distance between the centers of the shafts, and you have the length required.

If possible to avoid it, connected shafts should never be placed one directly over the other, as in such case the belt must be kept very tight to do the work.

It is desirable that the angle of the belt with the floor should not exceed 45 degrees. It is also desirable to locate the shafting and machinery so that belts should run from each shaft in opposite directions, as this arrangement will relieve the bearings from the friction that would result when the belts all pull one way on the shaft.

To Find the Belt Speed in Feet per Minute

Multiply diameter of pulley (in inches) by 3.1416. This gives circumference of pulley and this result multiplied by number of revolutions will give you belt speed in inches.

Relative Transmission of Horse Power for Any Given Width of Belt

The horse power for a given speed will be directly proportioned to the width of the belt; that is, a 4-ply, 16 inches wide, running at a certain speed, will transmit eight times as much power as a 4-ply belt, 2 inches wide, running at the same speed; and a belt 100 inches wide, ten times as much as a 10-inch belt of the same thickness, running at the same speed, etc.

To Find the Horse Power That Any Given Belt Will Transmit Economically

Multiply the width of the belt in inches by its speed in feet and divide the result by 800. The final result will be the horse power for a 4-ply belt. For a 6-ply belt, divide this result by 600; for an 8-ply, divide by 400; for a 10-ply, divide by 350.

To Find the Ply of a Belt of a Given Width Required

To transmit a given horse power economically, at a given belt speed, multiply the given horse power by 800 and the given width in inches by the given belt speed in feet and divide the first result by the second.

If the final result is one, or nearly one, a 4-ply belt is required; if one and one-half, a 6-ply; if one and three-quarters to two, an 8-ply; if two to two and one-quarter, a 10-ply.

To Find Width of Belt Required

To find the width of a 4-ply belt required to transmit a given horse power at a given belt speed per minute: Multiply the given horse power by 800, and divide the result by the given belt speed.

To find the width of a 6-ply belt required: Multiply horse power by 600; divide result by belt speed.

To find the width of an 8-ply belt required: Multiply horse power by 400; divide result by belt speed.

To find the width of a 10-ply belt required: Multiply horse power by 350; divide result by belt speed.

To Find Speed and Diameter of Pulleys

The product of the diameter and speed of the driving pulley equals the product of the diameter and speed of the driven pulley; consequently, if the speed and the diameter of the driving pulley are given, multiply them together and divide by the diameter of the driven pulley to find the speed of the driven; or divide by the speed of the driven pulley to find its diameter.

Example—The drive pulley on a tractor is 9½ inches in diameter and runs at 1,000 R. P. M.; what size pulley must be used on a thresher cylinder shaft that must run 1,100 R. P. M.?

9½ times 1,000 equals 9,500; divided by 1,100, equals 8.64. Since pulleys are made only in certain standard diameters, use either the next size larger, 9-inch diameter, and raise the engine speed slightly, or use 8½-inch pulley, considering that the slight slippage will reduce the effective speed to the correct number of revolutions per minute.

Example—At what speed will a rock crusher run, if its 6-inch pulley is belted to a 9½-inch pulley on a tractor with a R. P. M. of 1,000?

9½ times 1,000 equals 9,500; divided by 6, equals 1,583 R. P. M.

MEMORANDUM

MEMORANDUM

MEMORANDUM

MEMORANDUM

MEMORANDUM

MEMORANDUM

MEMORANDUM

MEMORANDUM